Candide

ST MARTIN'S PRESS NEW YORK

Voltaire's

CANDIDE

A Bilingual Edition

TRANSLATED AND EDITED BY

Peter Gay, YALE UNIVERSITY

Fourth Printing 1970

Library of Congress Catalog Card Number 63-10683

Manufactured in the United States of America

Designed by Alfred Manso

Introduction

THE WIT OF *Candide*

Candide is Voltaire's most famous book. His *Philosophical Dictionary* still has its readers; his pioneering historical works remain sources of delight and information to a small audience; his anticlerical polemics and humanitarian treatises furnish historians with valuable clues to shifts in eighteenth-century sensibilities; his brilliant correspondence is often quoted; while his tragedies, which made him the most famous literary man in Europe in his day, are now the preserve of the specialist. But *Candide* is read everywhere, in many languages and by many audiences. It has found many illustrators, including Paul Klee, whose spindly drawings capture the spare economy of Voltaire's prose; and its last line—*il faut cultiver notre jardin*—has become a philosophical cliché even for those whose French is rudimentary. In a word, *Candide* is that rare literary phenomenon, a classic in active cultural circulation.

This fame is easy to understand. For one thing, *Candide* is short. A born propagandist, Voltaire understood the virtues of brevity, and took complacent pride in the

effectiveness of his polemical pieces. In 1766, shortly after he had launched his *Philosophical Dictionary* (a relatively short book in its first edition), Voltaire, with a disparaging glance at Diderot's bulky Encyclopedia, observed: "Twenty folio volumes will never make a revolution. It's the small portable books at thirty *sous* that are dangerous. If the Gospel had cost 1,200 sesterces, the Christian religion would never have been established." *Candide* was part of the revolution Voltaire was making, and it compressed his message into a hundred pages.

What is more, *Candide* appears to be even shorter than it is, for Voltaire tells the tale with characteristic lightness of touch. His command of language makes his writings a superb model for the student of French. They reflect Voltaire's pleasure in words, his craftsman's readiness to revise and polish, his respect for style. But Voltaire wrote not merely to express himself, or to amuse, but to convince, too, and his language was at once an aim in itself and an instrument of persuasion.

Lightness of touch is another word for wit, and *Candide* is wit itself. It has often been objected that the characters in Voltaire's tales are lifeless, that they are puppets for whom it is impossible to feel anything. But this is not a failing, for it was not Voltaire's intention to make his characters into real people. He was writing in the age of Richardson's tearful epistolary novels and Diderot's equally tearful bourgeois dramas, but he turned to drier models—travel tales, picaresque stories, and *Gulliver's Travels*—to construct a genre combining

a minimum of sentimentality with a maximum of clear-headed aggressiveness. The narrator of *Candide*—or rather, the master of the puppets, for the narrator is invisible—throws his characters into the most improbable adventures, and his ironic detachment, coupled with the outrageous sequence of events, are both deliberate devices. The narrative machinery is as visible as the frame of a modern building, not because Voltaire lacked the skill to conceal it, but because he wanted it to be visible: when in Chapter 6 Pangloss is hanged at an *auto-da-fé*, he is hanged so that he may survive and reappear in Chapter 28; but Voltaire duly informs the reader that hanging is not customary at such affairs. The characters of *Candide* undergo gruesome experiences, but in Voltaire's hands these experiences are anything but gruesome: they happen too swiftly, they are told so coolly that no blood flows. The disemboweled are made whole and the dead are restored to life. Victims are raped, or flogged, or cut into pieces so quickly—one might almost say, so pleasantly—that the reader has no time to engage his sympathies. Even the dialogue, for all its natural flow, is anything but naturalistic; it is designed, like the story itself, to focus attention on ideas: " 'Do you think,' said Candide, 'that men have always massacred each other as they are doing today? That they have always been liars, crooks, traitors, ingrates, brigands, weaklings, unreliables, cowards, enviers, gluttons, drunkards, misers, social climbers, bloodsuckers, slanderers, debauchees, fanatics, hypocrites, and fools?' " Such speed invites, and almost compels the

reader to concentrate not on the sufferings of the characters but on the ludicrous disparity between their philosophy and their experience. The reader of *Candide* is purged not through pity and terror, but through thought. That is why the tale is properly called a philosophic tale.

Voltaire's economy of language and narrative speed have often been praised. Rightly so, for they permit him to master a sizable cast of characters and complicated sequence of events with complete ease, and to hit a wide variety of targets—sometimes two targets at once. When he calls Dr. Pangloss's seduction of a pretty chambermaid a "lesson in experimental physics," he touches, lightly and without prurience, on sexual matters (which always interest readers), and he spoofs, equally deftly, the prevailing rage for amateurish experiments. Again, when he gives an account of that chambermaid's syphilis, Voltaire lists a succession of men and women who have handed on the disease, but breaks the proper heterosexual chain at one point— "who owed it to a marquise, who had it from a page, who had got it from a Jesuit"—to strike a glancing blow at the supposed sexual proclivities of Jesuits and to parody at the same time the meticulous scholarship of the physician Astruc, who had written a treatise on venereal disease. Again, when Candide kills two of Cunégonde's lovers in Chapter 9, one an Inquisitor and the other a Jew named Don Issachar, Voltaire describes what happens when the bodies are discovered: "they bury Monseigneur in a beautiful church

and throw Issachar into the gutter." Thus, without holding up the narration for a moment, and with a single phrase, Voltaire introduces and castigates the Catholic practice of restricting burial in consecrated ground to certain persons. The chapter on Paris, the twenty-second, is the longest in the tale, made even longer than it originally was by an insertion of 1761. But it is not an inartistic intrusion: it advances the education of Candide while allowing Voltaire to defend one of his tragedies against criticism and to attack a number of literary and philosophical adversaries. This chapter, like all of *Candide*, teems with incident, but the incidents are always subsumed to the message: they may decorate the path, but they never turn it from its destination—those famous last words of the tale.

Some of Voltaire's wit, to be sure, was more obvious to his contemporaries than it is to us. Some of his allusions refer to controversies or events of the time that we must recall before we can fully appreciate *Candide*. In placing the opening of the tale in Westphalia, describing the place as a poverty-stricken accumulation of rustic hovels, and giving it the comical name of Thunder-ten-tronckh, Voltaire was feeding the vanity of cultured Europeans to whom German was a barbarous tongue, and to whom the German states were as barbarous as their language. Again, there is the second chapter which shows Candide as the prisoner of the Bulgarians and their king as a kindly monarch. Eighteenth-century readers had no difficulty iden-

tifying these "Bulgarians" as Prussians and their king as Frederick the Great. Nor could they fail to note the association of "Bulgar" to "bougre" or "bugger" —a word derived from the Latin *bulgarus*, the name for Bulgarians, who were widely known as Sodomites. Everyone who had followed Voltaire's friendship and quarrel with Frederick the Great must have smiled at this hint that the great military monarch might not be a lover of women. In Chapter 23 Candide witnesses the execution of a British admiral, shot for failing to sail close enough to the enemy. That victim, Voltaire's readers knew, was the British admiral John Byng, court-martialed and shot on 14 March 1757 for failing to relieve the British garrison at Minorca the previous year. Voltaire had tried to save him, in vain. The sardonic twenty-third chapter of *Candide* was his revenge on a world that would not listen to a humanitarian poet.

But it is remarkable to observe that these special references can be enjoyed even by those who fail to respond to their full bearing. Thunder-ten-tronckh is a funny name for all readers; and the Byng episode produced one of Voltaire's memorable *mots:* when Candide inquires why the admiral is being shot he is told that "in this country it is good to kill an admiral from time to time to encourage the others"—*pour encourager les autres.* This is perhaps the greatest virtue of Voltaire's wit: it is pointed and specific, but it enlarges the specific into the universal.

Voltaire wrote many other philosophic tales in addition to *Candide*, and with most of them it is hard to determine just when, where, and how he wrote them. In the eighteenth century, literary works often circulated in manuscript for years before they were committed to print, and the existence of several slightly divergent copies often obscures which is the first, "original" version of a work. Unscrupulous publishers further confused the record for posterity by bringing out inaccurate versions of pirated manuscripts. Besides, the age was one of capricious censorship and arbitrary arrests, so that authors with something impudent or subversive to say generally concealed their authorship and deliberately misled the public about the year and place of publication. Voltaire was a master of deception, and many of his works elude the kind of precise determination that delight the conscientious bibliographer. *Candide* offers many mysteries: its title page describes the tale as the work of one "Dr. Ralph," a German killed at the battle of Minden. Furthermore, Voltaire strenuously though unconvincingly denied throughout the spring of 1759 that he had written the book.

At the same time, Voltaire did not expect his readers to believe his denials. He would have been disappointed to be deprived of credit for a work he thought well of. Moreover, his style was unmistakable, and to the initiated, the tale was a transparent record of

Voltaire's experiences, for Voltaire was accustomed to pouring his life directly into his work. What holds true of such great polemics as the *Philosophical Dictionary* holds true of the best of his tales: they reflect what he had written, read, and thought about for years. That is why *Candide* becomes the more comprehensible the more we know of Voltaire's life as a whole.

Voltaire was born François-Marie Arouet in Paris, on 21 November 1694. His parents, prosperous middle-class bourgeois with some claim to aristocratic status and with excellent social connections, sent the gifted boy to *Louis-le-Grand*, a Paris *collège* to which the most aristocratic Parisian society sent its sons. It was at this fine Jesuit school that François-Marie made some lifelong friends, acquired his love for the classics, and first displayed his gift for language. His father wanted him to study law, and when that failed, to take up diplomacy, but the young man stubbornly frequented fashionable impious circles of aging roués whom he amused with his wit and his obvious talent for poetry.

François-Marie Arouet had found his vocation—literature—and over the next fifteen years that vocation brought great fame and grave vexation. In 1717–18 he spent eleven relatively painless months in the Bastille (a prison that could be comfortable for prisoners with money and connections) for some impudent verses against the Regent which he was perfectly capable of writing, although its authorship remains uncertain to this day. He emerged with his first tragedy, *Oedipe*,

and a new aristocratic name, "de Voltaire." The success of *Oedipe* in 1718 (which led theater-goers parched for dramatic talent to acclaim him as the heir of Corneille and Racine), fixed his new name in the public mind. Voltaire enhanced his literary reputation in the early 1720's with the first version of a long epic poem on Henri IV, significantly Voltaire's favorite king for his lack of religious fanaticism and his policy of religious toleration. But he was not allowed to bear his new name without challenge: late in 1725, it was publicly derided by a dissolute aristocrat, the Chevalier de Rohan. The quarrel smouldered all winter, and in February 1726 Voltaire was lured from a dinner party and beaten by Rohan's men. The incident brought Voltaire to the Bastille again, largely for protective custody. He was soon freed, banished from Paris, and in his anger and humiliation, undertook to visit England. He landed there in May 1726: a famous poet, a celebrated wit, a popular guest, but, after the Rohan episode, nothing more than a bourgeois against whom his former aristocratic friends had closed ranks.

England came as a powerful and salutary shock. Voltaire spent more than two years there, talking, observing, and writing; he came to appreciate the virtues of religious diversity, the energy of the commercial classes, the political power of the House of Commons, the intellectual splendor of its philosophical scientists and scientific philosophers, the arguments of the English Deists, and (perhaps most important of all) the high social and comfortable financial position of men

of letters. This is a nation, he wrote to a friend late in 1726 in his recently acquired English, "fond of their liberty, learned, witty, despising life and death, a nation of philosophers." The fruit of his visit was a lifelong affection for things English, which he jokingly called his "Anglomania," an unwavering admiration for the scientific system of Newton and the empiricist philosophy of Locke, a permanent commitment to Deism, and an equally enduring belief in the virtues of toleration and free speech. England did not create these Voltairian convictions, but it sharpened his radicalism by proving to him that what he had earlier considered Utopian hopes were practical realities. When he returned to France late in 1728, he brought with him notes for a book on England, a new tragedy on Brutus, and the draft of a historical work, his first, on King Charles xii of Sweden.

The book on England, the *Philosophical Letters*, which were published in France in 1734 after some dramatic triumphs in the theater, won Voltaire glorious notoriety: the book was immediately suppressed. Voltaire enjoyed the notoriety but prudently fled its consequences: by late spring of 1734 he was settled at Cirey, in Champagne, at the château of his mistress, Madame du Châtelet. Voltaire lived at Cirey for fifteen years, with interruptions for trips to Paris, Holland, and the Prussian court. There, during his middle years, he completed his education. With Madame du Châtelet, a love-starved bluestocking with a great flair for mathematics, languages, and technical philosophy,

Voltaire studied physics, mathematics, the philosophy of Leibnitz, and the higher Biblical criticism. It was a fruitful period, during which Voltaire published his distinguished popularization of Newton's thought, the *Elements of Newton's Philosophy*; began his great cultural histories, including his two masterpieces, the *Age of Louis XIV* and the *Essay on Manners*; and launched a new genre, the philosophic tale, of which *Candide* was to be a late, brilliant specimen.

The Cirey period clarified his philosophical views, deepened his political understanding, and intensified his religious radicalism. Many of the ideas he later expressed in *Candide* took form in these years. Yet the Voltaire of the 1740's could not have written *Candide*; he had to undergo much suffering before he was ready for his final settlement with "optimism." His public life had brought him triumph after triumph: in 1745 he had been named Royal Historiographer, and in the following year, after a shameless campaign, he was finally elected one of the Forty Immortals of the *Académie Française*. He had moments of doubt and depression, expressed most forcefully in his fine tale *Zadig*, written in 1747. But his real suffering began with a shock: the death of Madame du Châtelet in September 1749, in childbirth. Voltaire's idyl with Madame du Châtelet had been punctuated by quarrels, but the pair had a deep affection for one another. What was perhaps even worse than her death—which Voltaire bitterly mourned—was its cause: she had borne this child neither to her ostensible lover Vol-

taire, nor to her legal husband the Marquis du Châte-
let, but to a very minor minor poet, Saint-Lambert.

Worse was to come. Madame du Châtelet's death
freed Voltaire for some rather unfortunate political
adventures in Paris, and even more fatefully, for a
move to Prussia. By June 1750, Voltaire was in Pots-
dam, the permanent guest of his admirer, Frederick
of Prussia. The visit was not a success. True, at Pots-
dam Voltaire drafted his first openly anti-Christian
pamphlets and the first articles of what was to become
the *Philosophical Dictionary*. But while his work went
well, philosopher-poet and philosopher-king could not
get on with one another. Frederick was at once bril-
liant and harsh, half-worshipful and half-contemptuous
of his French visitor; Voltaire was at once servile and
independent, greedy and generous. Their close associa-
tion brought out what divided them, and it could
end only in separation. Early in 1753, Frederick and
Voltaire parted coldly, and did not resume correspond-
ence for several years.

The Prussian visit is written all over *Candide*. Vol-
taire was reminded of Frederick—if he had ever for-
gotten him—by Frederick's invasion of Saxony in
August 1756, an invasion that widened the undeclared
war between Britain and France into an all-European
conflict. The war that ensued, which proved to be the
destructive Seven Years War, supplied Voltaire with
abundant material for reflection on the misery of man
and the rascality of princes. His correspondence of
these years is filled with exclamations of dismay, and

with pacifist lamentations. Apparently it was sometime in 1757 that Voltaire began to set down some autobiographical reflections which deal mainly with his visit in Prussia, and offer a brilliantly malicious portrait of the Prussian king. These *Memoirs of Voltaire, written by himself*, are a dramatic reworking of his disillusioning experiences with Frederick, and thus a clue to *Candide*, over which Frederick ("king of the Bulgars") hangs like a nightmare.[1]

The sardonic pessimism of the *Memoirs* must be understood not only in the light of Voltaire's memories of Prussia, but also in the light of the whole philosophical question of "optimism," which had been raised in peculiarly poignant form by the Lisbon earthquake. I say "peculiarly poignant," for news of the irrational destructiveness of the earthquake of 1 November 1755, which killed more than thirty thousand people, reached Voltaire at *Les Délices*, his new house in Geneva. After his disastrous visit to Prussia, Voltaire had been a restless, homeless vagabond, and it was not until the winter of 1754–55 that he settled down once again. The news of the Lisbon earthquake came just as he was beginning to acquire a new sense of stability; soon after, the horrors of the Seven Years War began to haunt him. Late in 1758, he acquired Ferney, in French territory not far from *Les Délices*,

[1] The close relation of Voltaire's *Memoirs* to *Candide* has been searchingly explored by Ira O. Wade. See *Voltaire and Candide* (Princeton, Princeton University Press, 1959), pp. 132–41.

which became his permanent home during the last twenty years of his life: it was from Ferney that he launched his campaign to *écraser l'infâme* and to rescue victims of the French legal code; and it was from Ferney that he launched his *Philosophical Dictionary* and deluged the world, early in 1759, with denials that he had written *Candide*.

It is an obvious thing to say that Voltaire wrote *Candide* when he was ready to write it; not before and not after. But it remains pertinent to observe how much of his earlier life went into it—his Anglomania modified by disenchanted wit, his anticlericalism, his literary and political battles. Moreover, the Voltaire of the late 1750's was in a peculiar emotional tension: the death of Madame du Châtelet, the Lisbon earthquake, the behavior of Frederick were all sources of despair; at the same time, settling down, repairing houses, designing gardens in a delightful neighborhood were causes for happiness. *Candide* expresses this duality beautifully. The book scorns all the illusions of hope, yet triumphs over despair.

That note of despair is real enough. Voltaire had wrestled with philosophical optimism for many years. As early as 1736, the year he began his fateful correspondence with Frederick, he had expressed doubts about the philosophy of "whatever is, is right." Sometime in 1744, he wrote to a Göttingen professor named Martin Kahle, "When you have demonstrated, in verse or otherwise, why so many men butcher one another in the best of possible worlds, I shall be much obliged

to you." Then, early in the 1750's, he wrote the *Voyages of Scarmentado*, a relatively insignificant little tale, important mainly as a rehearsal for *Candide*. But it was the Lisbon earthquake, which called forth widespread consternation and earnest theological discussion, that compelled Voltaire to come to terms, once and for all, with notions of pre-established harmony or the consolation that the evils of this world serve a greater good. "Ultimately," as Ira Wade has put it, "the choice lay between Christian Providentialism, scientific materialism, and skepticism. What Voltaire had wished to do was to save the doctrine of Providence without the dogma of Christianity, science without materialism, and intellectual skepticism without the inactivity of Pyrrhonism. That was why optimism had so strongly appealed to him. But the earthquake, which made optimism so untenable, posed anew the question of choice." [2] In his anguish and uncertainty, Voltaire wrote the *Poem on the Lisbon Earthquake* which, as the subtitle makes explicit, is "an inquiry into the maxim, 'Whatever is, is right.'" With grim consistency, Voltaire rejects any attempt to console the unhappy survivors with philosophical panaceas: no system, he argues in his disheartened survey, is adequate to the terrors of human experience. Skepticism appears as the only answer: all man has left is doubt, resignation, and (almost as an afterthought) hope.

[2] *Ibid.*, p. 105.

The Lisbon Poem was not Voltaire's last word. Hope, with which he had ended the poem, seemed to him almost fatuous; resignation, too passive. In the years that followed the poem, which he had written at great speed soon after the earthquake, he took up once again the little compendium he had begun at Potsdam. We have little direct evidence from the correspondence, but it is clear from the texts of *Candide* and the *Philosophical Dictionary* that he was working on both at the same time: the mood of both works is a buoyant belligerence.[3]

[3] As far as I know, the intimate connection of these two major works has never been explored. But consider only these obvious parallels: Voltaire's argument on final causes in Chapter 1 of *Candide*, and his statement on the same subject in "Fin, Causes Finales" in the *Dictionnaire philosophique*; his hatred of war expressed in Chapter 3, and the same in the article "Guerre" of the *Dictionnaire*: "The marvelous part of this infernal enterprise is that every murderer's chief has his flags blessed, and solemnly invokes the Lord before he goes out to exterminate his neighbors." The list of kings in Chapter 30 (note 6) offers further evidence that Voltaire was thinking about and writing the *Dictionnaire philosophique* while he was working on *Candide*. Compare the article "Histoire des Rois Juifs et Paralipomènes": "While the style of the Book of Kings and of Chronicles is divine, still, the actions reported in these histories are perhaps not so divine. David assassinates Uriah; Ishbosheth and Mephibosheth are assassinated; Absalom assassinates Amnon; Joab assassinates Absalom; Solomon assassinates Adonijah, his brother; Baasha assassinates Nadab; Zimri assassinates Elah; Omri assassinates Zimri; Ahab assassinates Naboth; Jehu assassinates Ahab and Joram; the inhabitants of Jerusalem assassinate Amaziah, son of Joash; Shallum, son of Jabesh, assassinates Zachariah, son of Jeroboam; Menahem assassinates Shallum, son

Like most masterpieces, *Candide* has many mean-ings. Voltaire pursues a number of themes—he de-fends some forms of final cause, he advocates paci-fism and humanitarianism, he fights private quarrels, and takes sides in the great public quarrels of eight-eenth-century France by indulging his biting anti-clericalism. But these themes are all illustrations of the central significance of *Candide*; and that signifi-cance, toward which the whole story, the whole at-tack on philosophical optimism, is directed, is fully revealed only in the last sentence: *il faut cultiver notre jardin*—we must cultivate our garden.

Yet this is the kind of sweeping answer that turns upon closer examination into a large question: pre-cisely how big is the garden we are enjoined to culti-vate? We are told to cultivate *our* garden, but how much in this world is ours? If we define what is ours narrowly, the injunction leads to an Epicurean indif-ference to the outside world, a cultivation of one's

of Jabesh; Pekah, son of Remaliah, assassinates Pekahiah, son of Menahem; Hoshea, son of Elah, assassinates Pekah, son of Remaliah. I pass over in silence many other minor assassinations. It must be admitted that if the Holy Spirit wrote this history, he didn't choose a very edifying subject." By the time *Candide* was finished, Voltaire had gone beyond the malice of the *Memoirs* and the pessimism of the Lisbon Poem to create a masterpiece that included and transcended them. See also Chap-ter 13, note 1; Chapter 16, note 5; and especially Chapter 30, note 5. There are many other parallels.

sensibilities and a cherishing of the private sphere of existence. If we define what is ours broadly, the injunction leads to a Stoic indifference to suffering coupled with the acceptance of public responsibility.

Now Voltaire was both Stoic and Epicurean, an admirer both of Marcus Aurelius and of Lucretius. Cicero, his favorite ancient, had taught him the virtues of a discriminating eclecticism. It follows that the search for the meaning of *Candide* does not promise to be simple. I submit that the most fruitful clue lies in the twenty years left to Voltaire after he published *Candide*. The rest of his life is the most authoritative commentary we can find on the famous sentence that concludes the tale.

These rich and lively twenty years show that if Voltaire was both Stoic and Epicurean, he was more of the first than of the second. Settled at Ferney, he was rich, famous, independent. Yet, without diminishing his zest for the drama or the ribald anecdote, Voltaire turned increasingly to larger causes. He had been a society wit, a famous playwright, a great historian, and he abandoned none of these roles. But his life came to be dominated by greater and more serious things: his fight against Christianity, his fight for victims of injustice, and his fight in behalf of the under-privileged. Both the peasants on his French estate and the unenfranchised citizens of Geneva benefited from his insistent meddling. "I am ashamed to be so happy in the midst of so many disasters," he wrote in 1759, the year of *Candide*. It was as though he was justifying

his wealth, his fame, his security—in a word, his happiness—by work.

Voltaire's admirers have sometimes portrayed him as an improbable saint, an unselfish laborer in the vineyard of humanitarianism. The true estimate, I think, is both more complicated and less cloying. His great campaign to *écraser l'infâme*—significantly, the phrase begins to haunt his letters not long after he had written *Candide*—was part of a large vision: a genuine hatred of superstition and cruelty and a serious preference for a secular world. It represented a carefully worked-out analysis of the causes of fanaticism —*l'infâme* was not merely superstition, but every religious doctrine that taught anything more than a natural religion, for every such doctrine, no matter how innocuous, carried the germs of discord and fratricide. At the same time, Voltaire's skirmishes with the Church, his ridicule of the Bible, and his disproofs of dogma were a delightful battle against powerful but weakening forces. Far from being a benign lover of all mankind, Voltaire had enemies, hated them, and enjoyed showering them with the arrows of his analytical intellect and cruel wit.

The same mixed motives appear in his great campaign in behalf of Calas, the Chevalier de La Barre, the Sirven family, and other victims of the French legal system. In these celebrated cases, in which Voltaire helped to rescue the persons (or sometimes the posthumous reputation) of Frenchmen unjustly convicted of improbable crimes, he established some im-

portant principles: he opposed the use of torture as a method of obtaining information or as a method of punishment, he advocated public trials, confrontation of witnesses, reduction in punishments, careful definition of crimes, and a whole host of humanitarian practices which have since become the practice of decent judicial systems everywhere. They were great campaigns, which spread Voltaire's reputation among thousands of Europeans who did not know, or did not care, that this man had also written some famous tragedies. But it is clear that while Voltaire engaged in these exhausting enterprises from a rational desire for decency and a passionate hatred of cruelty, he also enjoyed the celebrity they brought and relished the thought that he might score off some old enemies at the same time that he was helping the innocent and the oppressed. The Calas case is characteristic: late in October 1761, Marc-Antoine Calas, a moody young Huguenot who lived with his family in Toulouse, was found hanged in his father's shop. His father was accused of the murder, tortured, and executed in March 1762, even though it seemed extremely probable that the young man had committed suicide. Voltaire heard of the case late in March, and greeted it with a kind of malicious joy: if the father was in fact guilty, it would prove the lengths to which a Protestant fanatic was willing to go to prevent his son from turning Catholic; if the father was innocent, it would prove the vicious stupidity of Catholics who still believed that Protestants committed ritual murders. In either

case, the Calas affair was fodder for the campaign to *écraser l'infâme*. This is the note on which Voltaire began, but not how he ended: he came to believe in the father's innocence and to be horrified at the methods used at the trial. It may be that this very mixture of motives gave Voltaire's humanitarian involvement its strength, but it is his ability to rise from the petty to the great, from the particular to the universal, from personal revenge to humanitarian principle, that makes this involvement so admirable.

Voltaire, then, a very human Stoic, cultivated his garden by lending his passionate intelligence, impressive learning, and unmatched stylistic resources to humanitarian causes. His garden was as wide as the world, because all men are brothers, and "on this pile of mud" (as Voltaire liked to call this earth) we justify our existence by helping our brothers, who are as weak, as dependent, and as worthy of attention as we are ourselves.

This interpretation of the last sentence of *Candide* is supported by the announced purpose of the work, which is to undermine the doctrine of philosophical optimism. Now the "optimism" against which Voltaire argued, a kind of caricature of Leibnitz's metaphysics, struck him as the antithesis of optimism. It was, he wrote, the most passive kind of pessimism: if all is for the best in the best of all possible worlds, then action is impossible and even irrelevant. Evil that is explained away as partial good hurts just as much as real evil, and is less open to attack. This kind of opti-

mism paralyzes the will to reform and improve by removing the tension between what exists and what is desirable. If what appears to be desirable conflicts with what exists, the philosophical optimist must pronounce the desire as a Utopia, a chimerical wish for the impossible. Against this despairing optimism, Voltaire pitted the Stoic notion of work and of responsibility.

All this sounds a little earnest, a little humorless, but it is obvious from *Candide* that Voltaire came to this philosophy with humor and joy. His Stoic seriousness never drowned his Epicurean pleasure in pleasure. He continued to write plays, poems, and essays; the very battle was a joy. Indeed, Voltaire preached—by example rather than by precept—that the recognition of the truth that this world is filled with evils leads to a certain good humor. If this life is a desert, it is our duty to make an oasis in it; if this life is a shipwreck, we must rescue as many as we can, and not forget to sing in the lifeboats. This, I think, is the message of *Candide*; its continuing popularity rests not only on its wit, its pace, its color, but also on its enduring relevance. Life is still a desert, still a shipwreck, and our obligation to face this bravely and with humor is as great as it was two hundred years ago, when Voltaire wrote his little masterpiece.

PETER GAY

Columbia University

Note on the Text

Candide appeared early in 1759 and was frequently reprinted, with slight changes, in the following two years. Specialists are still arguing over which of the various editions was the first, but most likely it was the edition completed by Voltaire's Genevan publishers, the brothers Cramer, in January 1759. Except for the long addition in Chapter 22, the various changes are of interest only to the expert. They are discussed in the critical editions. Of these the best known is the edition by André Morize (Paris, Hachette, 1913), with an excellent introduction, careful listing of variants, and full notes. René Pomeau has recently brought out another critical edition, with new notes and an interesting introduction (Paris, Librairie Nizet, 1959). In preparing this edition I have used the useful school edition by O. R. Taylor (Oxford, Blackwell, 1942), and register my gratitude here.

The most notable books on *Candide* are by Ira O. Wade, *Voltaire and "Candide," A Study in the Fusion of History, Art, and Philosophy* (Princeton, Princeton University Press, 1959), and W. F. Bottiglia, *Voltaire's Candide, Analysis of a Classic* (Geneva, Droz, 1959).

Candide has been translated many times, and well.

I have consulted my predecessors, and have on occasion appropriated a happy phrase. No one can do Voltaire's style full justice in translation—that is why a bilingual edition is so useful—but it is worth trying. My own translation comes closest to Donald M. Frame's (Bloomington, Indiana University Press, 1961); as Frame has observed, Voltaire achieves his effects by rapid shifts of tenses, suppression of connectives, and deliberate use of repetitions. I have tried to reproduce these stylistic devices as faithfully as possible. But the masterpiece appears in its full glory on the left-hand page.

P. G.

Candide

Candide ou l'Optimisme

TRADUIT DE

L'ALLEMAND DE MONSIEUR LE DOCTEUR RALPH

AVEC LES ADDITIONS

QU'ON A TROUVÉES DANS LA POCHE

DU DOCTEUR, LORSQU'IL

MOURUT À MINDEN,

L'AN DE GRÂCE

1759

Candide, or Optimism

TRANSLATED FROM THE

GERMAN OF DR. RALPH

WITH THE ADDITIONS

FOUND IN THE DOCTOR'S

POCKETS WHEN HE

DIED AT MINDEN IN

THE YEAR OF OUR LORD

1759

Table

Contents

1

Chapitre Premier

Comment Candide Fut Élevé dans un Beau Château, et Comment Il Fut Chassé d'Icelui

Il y avait en Vestphalie, dans le château de Monsieur le baron de Thunder-ten-tronckh, un jeune garçon à qui la nature avait donné les mœurs les plus douces. Sa physionomie annonçait son âme. Il avait le jugement assez droit avec l'esprit le plus simple: c'est, je crois, pour cette raison qu'on le nommait Candide. Les anciens domestiques de la maison soupçonnaient qu'il était fils de la sœur de monsieur le baron et d'un bon et honnête gentilhomme du voisinage, que cette demoiselle ne voulut jamais épouser parce qu'il n'avait pu prouver que soixante et onze quartiers,[1] et que le reste de son arbre généalogique avait été perdu par l'injure du temps.

Monsieur le baron était un des plus puissants seigneurs de la Vestphalie, car son château avait une porte et des fenêtres. Sa grande salle même était ornée d'une tapisserie. Tous les chiens de ses basses-cours compo-

[1] Each "quartering" represents one generation of noble ancestors. Mademoiselle Cunégonde (see Ch. 10, p. 77), is given

First Chapter

How Candide Was Brought Up in a Handsome Country House and How He Was Chased from the Same

In Westphalia, in the country house of Monsieur the Baron of Thunder-ten-tronckh, there was a young man whom nature had given the gentlest of characters. His face revealed his soul. He had pretty good sense, with the simplest of intellects; it is for that reason, I believe, that he was called Candide. The old servants of the house suspected that he was the son of Monsieur the Baron's sister and of a good and honorable gentleman of the neighborhood, whom that lady would never marry because he could prove only seventy-one quarterings,[1] and the rest of his genealogical tree had been lost by the ravages of time.

Monsieur the Baron was one of the most powerful lords of Westphalia, for his country house had a door and windows. His Great Hall was even decorated with a tapestry. All the dogs of his stable-yards formed a pack

seventy-two quarterings, which would take her family tree back more than two thousand years.

saient une meute dans le besoin; ses palefreniers étaient ses piqueurs; le vicaire du village était son grand aumônier. Ils l'appelaient tous Monseigneur, et ils riaient quand il faisait des contes.

Madame la baronne, qui pesait environ trois cent cinquante livres, s'attirait par là une très grande considération, et faisait les honneurs de la maison avec une dignité qui la rendait encore plus respectable. Sa fille Cunégonde, âgée de dix-sept ans, était haute en couleur, fraîche, grasse, appétissante. Le fils du baron paraissait en tout digne de son père. Le précepteur Pangloss[2] était l'oracle de la maison, et le petit Candide écoutait ses leçons avec toute la bonne foi de son âge et de son caractère.

Pangloss enseignait la métaphysico-théologo-cosmolonigologie.[3] Il prouvait admirablement qu'il n'y a point d'effet sans cause, et que, dans ce meilleur des mondes possibles, le château de monseigneur le baron était le plus beau des châteaux et madame la meilleure des baronnes possibles.

"Il est démontré, disait-il, que les choses ne peuvent être autrement: car, tout étant fait pour une fin, tout est nécessairement pour la meilleure fin. Remarquez bien que les nez ont été faits pour porter des lunettes; aussi avons-nous des lunettes. Les jambes sont visible-

[2] The good doctor's name is derived from the Greek and means "all-tongue."

[3] *Candide's* assault on cosmic optimism—the complacent conviction that all is for the best in the best of all possible worlds—is a composite caricature of the philosophy of Gottfried Wilhelm

of hounds when necessary; his grooms were his hunts-men; the village vicar was his Grand Almoner. They all called him "Monseigneur" and they laughed when he told stories.

Madame the Baroness, who weighed around three hundred and fifty pounds, thereby won very great re-spect, and did the honors of the house with a dignity which made her even more respectable. Her daughter Cunégonde, seventeen years old, was rosy-cheeked, fresh, buxom, appetizing. The Baron's son appeared in every-thing worthy of his father. Pangloss,[2] the tutor, was the oracle of the house, and little Candide listened to his lessons with all the trust of his age and character.

Pangloss taught metaphysico-theologo-cosmolo-nigol-ogy.[3] He proved admirably that there is no effect with-out a cause, and that, in this best of all possible worlds, the country house of Monseigneur the Baron was the handsomest of country houses, and Madame the best of possible Baronesses.

"It is demonstrated," he said, "that things cannot be otherwise; for, since everything was made for an end, all is necessarily for the best end. Note well that noses were made to wear spectacles; thus we have spectacles. Legs

von Leibnitz (1646–1716), Alexander Pope (1688–1744) whose work Voltaire knew, admired, and imitated, and Christian Wolff (1679–1754), a rigidly systematic German thinker who seems to have launched the popularity of the word "cosmology." One commentator, Donald M. Frame, suggests that "nigology" is supposed to suggest the French word *nigaud*—booby.

ment instituées pour être chaussées, et nous avons des chausses. Les pierres ont été formées pour être taillées et pour en faire des châteaux; aussi monseigneur a un très beau château; le plus grand baron de la province doit être le mieux logé; et, les cochons étant faits pour être mangés, nous mangeons du porc toute l'année: [4] par conséquent, ceux qui ont avancé que tout est bien ont dit une sottise; il fallait dire que tout est au mieux."

Candide écoutait attentivement, et croyait innocemment: car il trouvait Mademoiselle Cunégonde extrêmement belle, quoiqu'il ne prît jamais la hardiesse de le lui dire. Il concluait qu'après le bonheur d'être né baron de Thunder-ten-tronckh, le second degré de bonheur était d'être Mademoiselle Cunégonde; le troisième, de la voir tous les jours; et le quatrième, d'entendre maître Pangloss, le plus grand philosophe de la province, et par conséquent de toute la terre.

Un jour, Cunégonde, en se promenant auprès du château, dans le petit bois qu'on appelait parc, vit entre des broussailles le docteur Pangloss qui donnait une leçon de physique expérimentale à la femme de chambre de sa mère, petite brune très jolie et très docile. Comme Mademoiselle Cunégonde avait beaucoup de disposition pour les sciences, elle observa sans souffler les expériences réitérées dont elle fut témoin; elle vit clairement la raison suffisante [5] du docteur, les

[4] Voltaire did not wholly reject the argument of a final cause, that things in this world had been created for a purpose, but he ridiculed what he considered the misuse of the argument.

were obviously created to be breeched, and thus we have breeches. Stones were formed to be cut and made into country houses; thus Monseigneur has a very handsome country house; the greatest Baron of the province must be the best housed; and, since pigs were made to be eaten, we eat pork all year round.[4] Consequently, those who have argued that all is well have talked nonsense; they should have said all is for the best."

Candide listened attentively, and believed innocently, for he thought Mademoiselle Cunégonde extremely beautiful, although he never found courage to tell her so. He concluded that next to having been born Baron of Thunder-ten-tronckh, the second degree of happiness was to be Mademoiselle Cunégonde; the third, to see her every day; and the fourth, to listen to Master Pangloss, the greatest philosopher of the province, and consequently of the whole world.

One day, Cunégonde, taking a walk near the country house, in the little forest they called Park, saw in the bushes Doctor Pangloss giving a lesson in experimental physics to her mother's chambermaid, a very pretty and very docile little brunette. Since Mademoiselle Cunégonde had a great inclination for the sciences, she observed breathlessly the repeated experiments she witnessed; she clearly saw the Doctor's sufficient reason,[5] the effects and the causes, and returned

[5] Voltaire often amused himself at the expense of this Leibnitzian phrase, which he considered as nothing more than metaphysical jargon for "cause."

effets et les causes, et s'en retourna tout agitée, toute pensive, toute remplie du désir d'être savante, songeant qu'elle pourrait bien être la raison suffisante du jeune Candide, qui pouvait aussi être la sienne.

Elle rencontra Candide en revenant au château, et rougit; Candide rougit aussi; elle lui dit bonjour d'une voix entrecoupée, et Candide lui parla sans savoir ce qu'il disait. Le lendemain, après le dîner, comme on sortait de table, Cunégonde et Candide se trouvèrent derrière un paravent; Cunégonde laissa tomber son mouchoir, Candide le ramassa; elle lui prit innocemment la main, le jeune homme baisa innocemment la main de la jeune demoiselle avec une vivacité, une sensibilité, une grâce toute particulière; leurs bouches se rencontrèrent, leurs yeux s'enflammèrent, leurs genoux tremblèrent, leurs mains s'égarèrent. Monsieur le baron de Thunder-ten-tronckh passa auprès du paravent, et, voyant cette cause et cet effet, chassa Candide du château à grands coups de pied dans le derrière; Cunégonde s'évanouit; elle fut souffletée par madame la baronne dès qu'elle fut revenue à elle-même; et tout fut consterné dans le plus beau et le plus agréable des châteaux possibles.

home all excited, all pensive, all filled with the desire of being learned, thinking that she might well be the sufficient reason of young Candide, who might also be hers.

She met Candide in returning to the country house, and blushed; Candide blushed too; she said hello to him in a faltering voice, and Candide spoke to her without knowing what he was saying. The next day, after dinner, as people were leaving the table, Cunégonde and Candide found themselves behind a screen; Cunégonde dropped her handkerchief, Candide picked it up; she innocently took his hand; the young man innocently kissed the young lady's hand with a highly special vivacity, sensitivity, and grace; their lips met, their eyes sparkled, their knees trembled, their hands wandered. Monseigneur the Baron of Thunder-ten-tronckh passed near the screen, and, seeing this cause and that effect, drove Candide from the country house with great kicks in the behind; Cunégonde fainted; she was slapped by Madame the Baroness as soon as she revived; and all was in consternation in the handsomest and most agreeable of all possible country houses.

Chapitre Second

Ce Que Devint Candide Parmi les Bulgares[1]

Candide, chassé du paradis terrestre, marcha longtemps sans savoir où, pleurant, levant les yeux au ciel, les tournant souvent vers le plus beau des châteaux, qui renfermait la plus belle des baronnettes; il se coucha sans souper au milieu des champs entre deux sillons; la neige tombait à gros flocons. Candide, tout transi, se traîna le lendemain vers la ville voisine, qui s'appelle Valdberghoff-trarbk-dikdorff, n'ayant point d'argent, mourant de faim et de lassitude. Il s'arrêta tristement à la porte d'un cabaret. Deux hommes habillés de bleu le remarquèrent. "Camarade, dit l'un, voilà un jeune homme très bien fait, et qui a la taille requise." Ils s'avancèrent vers Candide et le prièrent à dîner très civilement. "Messieurs, leur dit Candide avec une modestie charmante, vous me faites beaucoup d'honneur, mais je n'ai pas de quoi payer mon écot. — Ah! Monsieur, lui dit un des bleus, les personnes de votre

[1] For the meaning of "Bulgarians," see the Introduction. The opposing nation, the Abarians, here representing France, were a

Second Chapter

What Became of Candide among the Bulgarians [1]

Candide, driven from the earthly paradise, walked for a long time without knowing where, crying, lifting his eyes to heaven, often turning them toward the handsomest of country houses, which contained the most beautiful of all Baronnettes; he slept without dining in the midst of the fields between two furrows; the snow fell in large flakes. The next day Candide, all numb, dragged himself toward the neighboring village, which was called Valdberghoff-trarbk-dikdorff, with no money, dying of hunger and fatigue. He stopped sadly at the door of an inn. Two men dressed in blue noticed him. "Comrade," said one, "here's a very well-built young man, and of the right height." They advanced towards Candide, and very civilly asked him to dinner. — "Gentlemen," Candide said to them with charming modesty, "you do me great honor, but I don't have the money to pay my share." — "Ah!

Scythian tribe about which Voltaire writes in his *Essai sur les moeurs*, *Oeuvres*, XI, 284.

figure et de votre mérite ne payent jamais rien: n'avez-vous pas cinq pieds cinq pouces de haut? — Oui, Messieurs, c'est ma taille, dit-il en faisant la révérence. — Ah! Monsieur, mettez-vous à table; non seulement nous vous défrayerons, mais nous ne souffrirons jamais qu'un homme comme vous manque d'argent; les hommes ne sont faits que pour se secourir les uns les autres. — Vous avez raison, dit Candide: c'est ce que Monsieur Pangloss m'a toujours dit, et je vois bien que tout est au mieux." On le prie d'accepter quelques écus, il les prend et veut faire son billet; on n'en veut point, on se met à table: "N'aimez-vous pas tendrement? . . . — Oh! oui, répond-il, j'aime tendrement Mademoiselle Cunégonde. — Non, dit l'un de ces messieurs, nous vous demandons si vous n'aimez pas tendrement le roi des Bulgares. — Point du tout, dit-il, car je ne l'ai jamais vu. — Comment! c'est le plus charmant des rois, et il faut boire à sa santé. — Oh! très volontiers, Messieurs"; et il boit. "C'en est assez, lui dit-on, vous voilà l'appui, le soutien, le défenseur, le héros des Bulgares; votre fortune est faite, et votre gloire est assurée." On lui met sur-le-champ les fers aux pieds, et on le mène au régiment. On le fait tourner à droite, à gauche, hausser la baguette, remettre la baguette, coucher en joue, tirer, doubler le pas, et on lui donne trente coups de bâton; le lendemain, il fait l'exercice un peu moins mal, et il ne reçoit que vingt coups; le surlendemain, on ne lui en donne que dix, et il est regardé par ses camarades comme un prodige.

monsieur," one of the men in blue said to him, "persons of your appearance and merit never pay anything; aren't you five feet five tall?" — "Yes, gentlemen, that's my height," he said, making a bow. "Ah! sir, sit down to dinner; not only will we pay your expenses, but we'll never allow a man like you to be without money; men are made only to help one another." — "You are right," said Candide; "that's what Monsieur Pangloss has always told me, and I see clearly that all is for the best." He is urged to accept a few *écus*, he takes them and wants to write a promissory note; they don't want it, they sit down to dinner. "Don't you love tenderly . . . ?" — "Oh! yes," he replied, "I tenderly love Mademoiselle Cunégonde." — "No," said one of these gentlemen. "We are asking you if you don't tenderly love the King of the Bulgarians?" — "Not at all," he said, "for I've never seen him." — "What! He's the most charming of kings, and we must drink to his health." — "Oh! very gladly, gentlemen." And he drinks. "That's enough," he is told, "you are now the aid, the support, the defender, the hero of the Bulgarians; your fortune is made, and your glory is assured." At once they put irons on his legs, and lead him to the regiment. They make him turn right, left, raise the ramrod, lower the ramrod, take aim, fire, march at double time, and they give him thirty strokes with a stick; the next day he drills a little less badly, and receives only twenty strokes; the day after that, they give him only ten, and he is regarded by his comrades as a prodigy.

Candide, tout stupéfait, ne démêlait pas encore trop bien comment il était un héros. Il s'avisa, un beau jour de printemps, de s'aller promener, marchant tout droit devant lui, croyant que c'était un privilège de l'espèce humaine, comme de l'espèce animale, de se servir de ses jambes à son plaisir. Il n'eut pas fait deux lieues que voilà quatre autres héros de six pieds qui l'atteignent, qui le lient, qui le mènent dans un cachot. On lui demanda juridiquement ce qu'il aimait le mieux d'être fustigé trente-six fois par tout le régiment, ou de recevoir à la fois douze balles de plomb dans la cervelle. Il eut beau dire que les volontés sont libres et qu'il ne voulait ni l'un ni l'autre, il fallut faire un choix; il se détermina, en vertu du don de Dieu qu'on nomme liberté, à passer trente-six fois par les baguettes; [2] il essuya deux promenades. Le régiment était composé de deux mille hommes; cela lui composa quatre mille coups de baguette, qui, depuis la nuque du cou jusqu'au cul, lui découvrirent les muscles et les nerfs. Comme on allait procéder à la troisième course, Candide, n'en pouvant plus, demanda en grâce qu'on voulût bien avoir la bonté de lui casser la tête: il obtint cette faveur; on lui bande les yeux, on le fait mettre à genoux. Le roi des Bulgares passe dans ce moment, s'informe du crime du patient; et, comme ce roi avait un grand génie, il comprit, par tout ce qu'il apprit de

[2] Here, as elsewhere, Voltaire utilizes his experience at the court of Frederick the Great. In his *Memoirs*, he speaks of Prussian soldiers who were "made to run the gauntlet thirty-six times

Candide, completely bewildered, did not yet figure out too clearly how he was a hero. One fine spring day he took it into his head to go strolling, walking straight ahead of him, believing that it was a privilege of the human species, as of animal species, to use its legs as it pleased. He had not gone five miles when there appear four other six-footed heroes who catch up with him, who tie him up, who put him into a dungeon. He was asked juridically whether he preferred to be beaten thirty-six times by the whole regiment or to receive twelve balls of lead in his brain all at once. In vain he told them that wills are free and that he wanted neither the one nor the other, he had to make a choice; he made up his mind by virtue of the gift of God called *liberty* to run the gauntlet thirty-six times; [2] he walked through it twice. The regiment was made up of two thousand men. That made four thousand strokes of the ramrod for him, which laid open his muscles and his nerves from the nape of the neck down to his behind. As they got ready for the third run through, Candide, who could go on no more, asked as a favor that they be good enough to smash in his head; he was granted that favor; they blindfold him; they make him get down on his knees. At that moment the King of the Bulgarians passes by, inquires about the culprit's crime; and since this King had great genius, he understood, from everything he learned from

under the windows of the monarch who looked at them."
Oeuvres, I, 29.

Candide, que c'était un jeune métaphysicien fort ignorant des choses de ce monde, et il lui accorda sa grâce avec une clémence qui sera louée dans tous les journaux et dans tous les siècles.[3] Un brave chirurgien guérit Candide en trois semaines avec les émollients enseignés par Dioscoride.[4] Il avait déjà un peu de peau et pouvait marcher, quand le roi des Bulgares livra bataille au roi des Abares.

[3] This, too, is a reminiscence, referring to a French gentleman, kidnapped into the Prussian army, who deserted, was captured and imprisoned at Spandau. His name was Courtils, and he was released upon Voltaire's representations. See *Oeuvres*, I, 30–31.

Candide, that this was a young metaphysician quite ignorant of the things of this world, and he granted him his pardon with the clemency that will be praised in all the newspapers and in all centuries.[3] A decent surgeon cured Candide in three weeks with the ointments invented by Dioscorides.[4] He already had a little skin, and could march, when the King of the Bulgarians gave battle to the King of the Abarians.

[4] Pedanius Dioscorides, famous Greek physician of the first century A.D., who served in the Roman army and whose book on materia medica remained a standard reference work for several centuries.

Chapitre Troisième

Comment Candide Se Sauva d'Entre les Bulgares, et ce Qu'Il Devint

Rien n'était si beau, si leste, si brillant, si bien ordonné que les deux armées. Les trompettes, les fifres, les hautbois, les tambours, les canons, formaient une harmonie telle qu'il n'y en eut jamais en enfer. Les canons renversèrent d'abord à peu près six mille hommes de chaque côté; ensuite la mousqueterie ôta du meilleur des mondes environ neuf à dix mille coquins qui en infectaient la surface. La baïonnette fut aussi la raison suffisante de la mort de quelques milliers d'hommes. Le tout pouvait bien se monter à une trentaine de mille âmes. Candide, qui tremblait comme un philosophe, se cacha du mieux qu'il put pendant cette boucherie héroïque.

Enfin, tandis que les deux rois faisaient chanter des *Te Deum*, chacun dans son camp,[1] il prit le parti d'aller raisonner ailleurs des effets et des causes. Il passa par-

[1] This whole chapter, which bears the stamp of Voltaire's angry pacifism, reflects his horror at the Seven Years War. He

Third Chapter

How Candide Escaped from among the Bulgarians and What Became of Him

Nothing could be so handsome, so smart, so brilliant, so well trained as the two armies. Trumpets, fifes, oboes, drums, cannon formed a harmony such as had never been in hell. First the cannon knocked down about six thousand men on each side; then the musketry took from the best of worlds around nine to ten thousand rascals who infested its surface. Also the bayonet was the sufficient reason for the death of several thousand men. The whole could well mount up to about thirty thousand souls. Candide, who trembled like a philosopher, hid himself as well as he could during this heroic butchery.

Finally, while the two Kings had *Te Deums* sung, each in his camp,[1] he decided to go reason elsewhere about effects and causes. He passed over piles of dead

often ridiculed the association of religious ceremony with military glory.

dessus des tas de morts et de mourants, et gagna d'abord un village voisin; il était en cendres: c'était un village abare que les Bulgares avaient brûlé, selon les lois du droit public. Ici des vieillards criblés de coups regardaient mourir leurs femmes égorgées, qui tenaient leurs enfants à leurs mamelles sanglantes; là des filles, éventrées après avoir assouvi les besoins naturels de quelques héros, rendaient les derniers soupirs; d'autres, à demi brûlées, criaient qu'on achevât de leur donner la mort. Des cervelles étaient répandues sur la terre à côté de bras et de jambes coupés.

Candide s'enfuit au plus vite dans un autre village: il appartenait à des Bulgares, et les héros abares l'avaient traité de même. Candide, toujours marchant sur des membres palpitants ou à travers des ruines, arriva enfin hors du théâtre de la guerre, portant quelques petites provisions dans son bissac, et n'oubliant jamais Mademoiselle Cunégonde. Ses provisions lui manquèrent quand il fut en Hollande; [2] mais, ayant entendu dire que tout le monde était riche dans ce pays-là et qu'on y était chrétien, il ne douta pas qu'on ne le traitât aussi bien qu'il l'avait été dans le château de monsieur le baron, avant qu'il en eût été chassé pour les beaux yeux de Mademoiselle Cunégonde.

Il demanda l'aumône à plusieurs graves personnages, qui lui répondirent tous que, s'il continuait à faire ce métier, on l'enfermerait dans une maison de correction pour lui apprendre à vivre.

[2] Voltaire greatly admired the United Provinces for their wealth, their toleration, and their relative social equality.

and dying, and first reached a neighboring village; it was in ashes; this was an Abarian village which the Bulgarians had burned according to the rules of international law. Here, old men, dazed by blows, watched their butchered wives dying, holding their children to their bleeding breasts; there, girls, disemboweled after they had satisfied the natural needs of a few heroes, breathed their last sighs; others, half burned, begged to be put to death. Brains were scattered over the ground beside severed arms and legs.

Candide fled as fast as possible into another village; it belonged to the Bulgarians, and the Abarian heroes had treated it in the same way. Candide, still stepping on quivering limbs, or across ruins, finally got away from the theater of war, carrying some small provisions in his knapsack, and never forgetting Mademoiselle Cunégonde. When he reached Holland his provisions were gone; [2] but having heard that everybody was rich in that country, and that they were Christians there, he did not doubt that he would be treated as well as he had been in the country house of Monseigneur the Baron before he had been chased out because of Mademoiselle Cunégonde's pretty eyes.

He asked for alms from several grave personages, who all replied to him that if he continued to carry on this business, he would be shut up in a house of correction to teach him how to live.

Il s'adressa ensuite à un homme qui venait de parler tout seul une heure de suite sur la charité dans une grande assemblée. Cet orateur, le regardant de travers, lui dit: "Que venez-vous faire ici? y êtes-vous pour la bonne cause? — Il n'y a point d'effet sans cause, répondit modestement Candide; tout est enchaîné nécessairement et arrangé pour le mieux. Il a fallu que je fusse chassé d'auprès de Mademoiselle Cunégonde, que j'aie passé par les baguettes, et il faut que je demande mon pain jusqu'à ce que je puisse en gagner; tout cela ne pouvait être autrement. — Mon ami, lui dit l'orateur, croyez-vous que le pape soit l'Antéchrist? — Je ne l'avais pas encore entendu dire, répondit Candide; mais, qu'il le soit ou qu'il ne le soit pas, je manque de pain. — Tu ne mérites pas d'en manger, dit l'autre; va, coquin; va, misérable, ne m'approche de ta vie." La femme de l'orateur, ayant mis la tête à la fenêtre et avisant un homme qui doutait que le pape fût antéchrist, lui répandit sur le chef un plein . . . O Ciel! à quel excès se porte le zèle de la religion dans les dames!

Un homme qui n'avait point été baptisé, un bon anabaptiste, nommé Jacques, vit la manière cruelle et ignominieuse dont on traitait ainsi un de ses frères, un être à deux pieds sans plumes, qui avait une âme; il l'amena chez lui, le nettoya, lui donna du pain et de la bière, lui fit présent de deux florins, et voulut même lui apprendre à travailler dans ses manufactures aux

Finally he addressed himself to a man who had just spoken about charity in a large assembly for a whole hour, all by himself. This orator, giving him a dark look, said to him: "What are you doing here? Are you here for the good cause?" — "There is no effect without cause," replied Candide modestly; "everything is necessarily linked, and arranged for the best. It was necessary for me to be chased away from Mademoiselle Cunégonde, to run the gauntlet, and it is necessary that I beg for my bread until I can earn it; all this could not have been otherwise." — "My friend," the orator told him, "do you believe that the Pope is Anti-Christ?" — "I have never even heard that before," replied Candide; "but, whether he is or not, I lack bread." — "You don't deserve to eat any," said the other; "get away, rascal; get away, wretch, don't ever come near me again." The orator's wife, having put her head out the window, and noticing a man who doubted that the Pope was Anti-Christ, poured over his head a full . . . O Heavens! To what excess religious zeal is carried in ladies!

A man who had not been baptized, a good Anabaptist called Jacques, saw the cruel and ignominious manner in which one of his brothers—a two-footed featherless being with a soul—was being treated; he took him home, cleaned him up, gave him some bread and beer, gave him a present of two florins, and even wanted to teach him to work in his factories of Persian

étoffes de Perse qu'on fabrique en Hollande.[3] Candide, se prosternant presque devant lui, s'écriait: "Maître Pangloss me l'avait bien dit que tout est au mieux dans ce monde, car je suis infiniment plus touché de votre extrême générosité que de la dureté de ce monsieur à manteau noir, et de madame son épouse."

Le lendemain, en se promenant, il rencontra un gueux tout couvert de pustules, les yeux morts, le bout du nez rongé, la bouche de travers, les dents noires, et parlant de la gorge, tourmenté d'une toux violente et crachant une dent à chaque effort.

[3] Voltaire thought that the sixteenth-century Anabaptists, a radical wing of the German Reformation which rejected infant baptism, were "bloody fanatics," but he considered their eighteenth-century successors the most peaceful and charitable of men. See *Essai sur les moeurs, Oeuvres*, XIII, 489–90.

stuff that is made in Holland.³ Candide, frantically falling at his feet before him, exclaimed: "Doctor Pangloss was right to tell me that all is for the best in this world, for I am infinitely more touched by your extreme generosity than by the harshness of that gentleman in the black coat, and of Madame, his wife."

The next day, taking a walk, he encountered a beggar all covered with sores, with lifeless eyes, the end of his nose rotted away, his mouth awry, his teeth black, and talking from his throat, tormented by a violent cough, and spitting out a tooth at each attack.

Chapitre Quatrième

Comment Candide Rencontra Son Ancien Maître de Philosophie, le Docteur Pangloss, et ce Qui en Advint

Candide, plus ému encore de compassion que d'horreur, donna à cet épouvantable gueux les deux florins qu'il avait reçus de son honnête anabaptiste Jacques. Le fantôme le regarda fixement, versa des larmes et sauta à son cou. Candide, effrayé, recule. "Hélas! dit le misérable à l'autre misérable, ne reconnaissez-vous plus votre cher Pangloss? — Qu'entends-je? Vous, mon cher maître! Vous, dans cet état horrible! Quel malheur vous est-il donc arrivé? Pourquoi n'êtes-vous plus dans le plus beau des châteaux? Qu'est devenue Mademoiselle Cunégonde, la perle des filles, le chef-d'œuvre de la nature? — Je n'en peux plus," dit Pangloss. Aussitôt Candide le mena dans l'étable de l'anabaptiste, où il lui fit manger un peu de pain; et quand Pangloss fut refait: "Eh bien! lui dit-il, Cunégonde? — Elle est morte," reprit l'autre. Candide s'évanouit à ce mot; son ami rappela ses sens avec un peu de mauvais vinaigre qui se trouva par hasard dans l'étable. Candide

Fourth Chapter

How Candide Met His Old Philosophy Teacher,
Doctor Pangloss, and What Came of It

Candide, even more moved by compassion than hor-
ror, gave this frightful beggar the two florins which he
had received from his honest Anabaptist, Jacques. The
phantom looked at him fixedly, shed some tears, and
threw his arms around his neck. Candide, terrified, re-
coils. "Alas!" says the wretch to the other wretch,
"don't you recognize your dear Pangloss any more?"
— "What do I hear? You, my dear teacher! You, in
this horrible condition! What misfortune, then, has
happened to you? Why are you no longer in the hand-
somest of country houses? What has become of Made-
moiselle Cunégonde, the pearl of girls, the masterpiece
of nature?" — "I am worn out," said Pangloss. Right
away Candide took him into the Anabaptist's stable
where he made him eat a little bread, and when
Pangloss had recovered: "All right!" he said to him,
"Cunégonde?" — "She is dead," replied the other. At
this word Candide fainted; his friend restored him to
his senses with a little bad vinegar which happened to

rouvre les yeux. "Cunégonde est morte! Ah! meilleur des mondes, où êtes-vous? Mais de quelle maladie est-elle morte? Ne serait-ce point de m'avoir vu chasser du beau château de monsieur son père à grands coups de pied? — Non, dit Pangloss; elle a été éventrée par des soldats bulgares, après avoir été violée autant qu'on peut l'être; ils ont cassé la tête à monsieur le baron, qui voulait la défendre; madame la baronne a été coupée en morceaux; mon pauvre pupille, traité précisément comme sa sœur; et quant au château, il n'est pas resté pierre sur pierre, pas une grange, pas un mouton, pas un canard, pas un arbre; mais nous avons été bien vengés, car les Abares en ont fait autant dans une baronnie voisine qui appartenait à un seigneur bulgare."

A ce discours, Candide s'évanouit encore; mais, revenu à soi et ayant dit tout ce qu'il devait dire, il s'enquit de la cause et de l'effet, et de la raison suffisante qui avaient mis Pangloss dans un si piteux état. "Hélas! dit l'autre, c'est l'amour; l'amour, le consolateur du genre humain; le conservateur de l'univers, l'âme de tous les êtres sensibles, le tendre amour. — Hélas! dit Candide, je l'ai connu, cet amour, ce souverain des cœurs, cette âme de notre âme; il ne m'a jamais valu qu'un baiser et vingt coups de pieds au cul. Comment cette belle cause a-t-elle pu produire en vous un effet si abominable?" Pangloss répondit en ces termes: "O mon cher Candide! vous avez connu Paquette, cette jolie suivante de notre auguste baronne; j'ai goûté dans ses bras les délices du paradis, qui ont

be in the stable. Candide reopens his eyes. "Cuné-gonde is dead! Ah! best of worlds, where are you? But what disease did she die of? Isn't it from having seen me expelled from the handsome country house of Monsieur, her father, with big kicks?" — "No," said Pangloss. "She was disemboweled by Bulgarian soldiers, after having been violated as much as she could be; they smashed in the head of Monsieur the Baron, who wanted to defend her; Madame the Baroness was cut into pieces; my poor pupil treated exactly like his sister; and as for the country house, not one stone remains on another, not a barn, not a sheep, not a duck, not a tree; but we have been well avenged, for the Abarians did exactly the same thing in a neighboring barony which belonged to a Bulgarian Lord."

At this report, Candide fainted again; but, having come back to his senses and said all that was called for, he inquired about the cause and effect, and about the sufficient reason that had put Pangloss into such a piteous state. "Alas!" said the other, "it's love; love, the consoler of mankind, preserver of the universe, soul of all feeling beings, tender love." — "Alas!" said Candide, "I have known it, this love, this sovereign of hearts, that soul of our soul; it has never brought me anything but a kiss and twenty kicks in the behind. How could this beautiful cause produce such an abominable effect in you?" Pangloss replied in these words: "Oh my dear Candide! You know Paquette, that pretty attendant of our august Baroness; in her arms I tasted the delights of Paradise which produced these torments

produit ces tourments d'enfer dont vous me voyez dévoré; elle en était infectée, elle en est peut-être morte. Paquette tenait ce présent d'un cordelier [1] très savant quit avait remonté à la source, car il l'avait eu d'une vieille comtesse, qui l'avait reçu d'un capitaine de cavalerie, qui le devait à une marquise, qui le tenait d'un page, qui l'avait reçu d'un jésuite qui, étant novice, l'avait eu en droite ligne d'un des compagnons de Christophe Colomb. Pour moi, je ne le donnerai à personne, car je me meurs."

"O Pangloss! s'écria Candide, voilà une étrange généalogie! n'est-ce pas le diable qui en fut la souche? — Point du tout, répliqua ce grand homme; c'était une chose indispensable dans le meilleur des mondes, un ingrédient nécessaire: car si Colomb n'avait pas attrapé dans une île de l'Amérique cette maladie qui empoisonne la source de la génération, qui souvent même empêche la génération, et qui est évidemment l'opposé du grand but de la nature, nous n'aurions ni le chocolat ni la cochenille; [2] il faut encore observer que jusqu'aujourd'hui, dans notre continent, cette maladie nous est particulière, comme la controverse. Les Turcs, les Indiens, les Persans, les Chinois, les Siamois, les Japonais, ne la connaissent pas encore; mais il y a une raison suffisante pour qu'ils la connaissent à leur tour dans quelques siècles. En attendant, elle a fait un merveilleux progrès parmi nous, et surtout dans ces

[1] Here, as elsewhere, the French designation *cordelier* has been translated as "Franciscan": the monks of the orders follow-

of Hell with which you see me devoured; she was infected with them, she may have died of them. Paquette got this present from a very learned Franciscan [1] who had gone back to the source, for he had it from an old countess, who had got it from a captain of cavalry, who owed it to a marquise, who had it from a page, who had got it from a Jesuit, who, being a novice, had it in a direct line from one of the companions of Christopher Columbus. As for myself, I'll never give it to anyone, for I am dying."

"O Pangloss!" Candide exclaimed, "Here's a strange genealogy! Isn't the devil at the root of it?" — "Not at all," replied that great man; "it was an indispensable thing in the best of worlds, a necessary ingredient; for if Columbus had not caught, in an island of America, that disease which poisons the source of generation, which often even prevents generation, and which is obviously the opposite of the great aim of nature, we would have neither chocolate nor cochineal; [2] it should also be noted that up to this date this disease is reserved to us in our continent, like controversy. The Turks, the Indians, the Persians, the Chinese, the Siamese, the Japanese do not yet know it; but there is a sufficient reason why they will know it in their turn in several centuries. Meanwhile it has made marvelous progress, and above all in those great armies made up

ing the rule of St. Francis may be distinguished by their rope belt. For the genealogy of syphilis, see the Introduction.

[2] An expensive, coveted scarlet dye, imported from Mexico and other Central American states in the eighteenth century.

grandes armées composées d'honnêtes stipendiaires bien élevés, qui décident du destin des États; on peut assurer que, quand trente mille hommes combattent en bataille rangée contre des troupes égales en nombre, il y a environ vingt mille vérolés de chaque côté."

"Voilà qui est admirable, dit Candide; mais il faut vous faire guérir. — Et comment le puis-je? dit Pangloss; je n'ai pas le sou, mon ami, et dans toute l'étendue de ce globe on ne peut ni se faire saigner, ni prendre un lavement sans payer, ou sans qu'il y ait quelqu'un qui paye pour nous."

Ce dernier discours détermina Candide; il alla se jeter aux pieds de son charitable anabaptiste Jacques, et lui fit une peinture si touchante de l'état où son ami était réduit que le bonhomme n'hésita pas à recueillir le docteur Pangloss; il le fit guérir à ses dépens. Pangloss, dans la cure, ne perdit qu'un œil et une oreille. Il écrivait bien et savait parfaitement l'arithmétique. L'anabaptiste Jacques en fit son teneur de livres. Au bout de deux mois, étant obligé d'aller à Lisbonne pour les affaires de son commerce, il mena dans son vaisseau ses deux philosophes. Pangloss lui expliqua comment tout était on ne peut mieux. Jacques n'était pas de cet avis. "Il faut bien, disait-il, que les hommes aient un peu corrompu la nature, car ils ne sont point nés loups, et ils sont devenus loups. Dieu ne leur a donné ni canon de vingt-quatre ni baïonnettes, et ils se sont fait des baïonnettes et des canons pour se détruire. Je pourrais mettre en ligne de compte les banqueroutes et la justice qui s'empare des biens des

of decent, well-educated mercenaries, which decide the destiny of states; we may be confident that when thirty thousand men fight in pitched battle against troops equal in number, there are about twenty thousand syphilitics on each side."

"Now that's admirable," said Candide; "but we must have you cured." — "And how can I be?" said Pangloss; "I don't have a sou, my friend, and in the whole extent of this globe, one can neither be bled nor take an enema without paying, or without having someone who pays for you."

This last speech made up Candide's mind; he went and threw himself at the feet of his charitable Anabaptist, Jacques, and painted such a touching picture of the condition to which his friend had been reduced that the good man did not hesitate to shelter Doctor Pangloss; he had him cured at his expense. In this cure, Pangloss lost only one eye and one ear. He wrote well and knew arithmetic perfectly. The Anabaptist Jacques made him his bookkeeper. At the end of two months, being obliged to go to Lisbon on matters of business, he brought his two philosophers along on his ship. Pangloss explained to him how everything was arranged for the best. Jacques was not of this opinion. "It must be," he said, "that men have corrupted nature a little, for they are not born as wolves, and they have become wolves. God has given them neither twenty-four-pounder cannons nor bayonets; and they have made themselves bayonets and cannons to destroy one another. I could take into account bankruptcies, and Justice which seizes the goods of the

banqueroutiers pour en frustrer les créanciers.[3] — Tout cela était indispensable, répliquait le docteur borgne, et les malheurs particuliers font le bien général,[4] de sorte que plus il y a de malheurs particuliers, et plus tout est bien." Tandis qu'il raisonnait, l'air s'obscurcit, les vents soufflèrent des quatre coins du monde, et le vaisseau fut assailli de la plus horrible tempête à la vue du port de Lisbonne.

[3] Voltaire's spleen against a system that imposes yet further losses on the creditors of bankrupts reflects his own losses in the bankruptcy of the banker Bernard in 1754.

bankrupts to defraud creditors of them." [3] — "All that was indispensable," replied the one-eyed doctor, "and private misfortunes make up the general good; [4] so that the more private misfortunes there are, the more all is well." While he was arguing, the air darkened, the winds blew from the four corners of the earth, and the vessel was assailed by the most horrible tempest in the sight of the port of Lisbon.

[4] This, of course, is one of the central formulations of the philosophical optimism that Voltaire is attacking.

Chapitre Cinquième

Tempête, Naufrage, Tremblement de Terre, et ce Qui Advint du Docteur Pangloss, de Candide et de l'Anabaptiste Jacques

La moitié des passagers affaiblis, expirants de ces angoisses inconcevables que le roulis d'un vaisseau porte dans les nerfs et dans toutes les humeurs du corps agitées en sens contraires, n'avait pas même la force de s'inquiéter du danger. L'autre moitié jetait des cris et faisait des prières; les voiles étaient déchirées, les mâts brisés, le vaisseau entr'ouvert. Travaillait qui pouvait, personne ne s'entendait, personne ne commandait. L'anabaptiste aidait un peu à la manœuvre; il était sur le tillac; un matelot furieux le frappe rudement et l'étend sur les planches; mais du coup qu'il lui donna il eut lui-même une si violente secousse qu'il tomba hors du vaisseau la tête la première. Il restait suspendu et accroché à une partie de mât rompue. Le bon Jacques court à son secours, l'aide à remonter, et de l'effort qu'il fit il est précipité dans la mer à la vue du matelot, qui le laissa périr sans daigner seulement le regarder. Candide approche, voit son bienfaiteur qui reparaît un

Fifth Chapter

Tempest, Shipwreck, Earthquake, and What Became of Dr. Pangloss, Candide and the Anabaptist Jacques

Half of the debilitated passengers, at death's door with those inconceivable agonies which the rolling of the vessel produces in the nerves, and all the humors of the body tossed in opposite directions, did not even have the strength to be concerned about the danger. The other half uttered screams and said prayers; the sails were torn, the masts broken to pieces, the vessel split. Whoever could, worked; nobody cooperated, nobody commanded. The Anabaptist helped the work a little; he was on the main deck; a maddened sailor struck him violently and dropped him on the plank; but from the blow he gave him, he himself got such a violent jolt that he fell from the vessel, head first. He was caught and remained dangling on a piece of the broken mast. Good Jacques runs to his aid, helps him to climb back up, and by the effort he makes he is thrown into the sea in sight of the sailor, who lets him perish without even deigning to look at him. Candide approaches, sees his benefactor who reappears

moment et qui est englouti pour jamais. Il veut se jeter
après lui dans la mer; le philosophe Pangloss l'en em-
pêche, en lui prouvant que la rade de Lisbonne avait
été formée exprès pour que cet anabaptiste s'y noyât.
Tandis qu'il le prouvait *a priori*, le vaisseau s'entr'ouvre,
tout périt à la réserve de Pangloss, de Candide, et de
ce brutal de matelot qui avait noyé le vertueux ana-
baptiste; le coquin nagea heureusement jusqu'au rivage,
où Pangloss et Candide furent portés sur une planche.

Quand ils furent revenus un peu à eux, ils mar-
chèrent vers Lisbonne; il leur restait quelque argent,
avec lequel ils espéraient se sauver de la faim après
avoir échappé à la tempête.

A peine ont-ils mis le pied dans la ville en pleurant
la mort de leur bienfaiteur, qu'ils sentent la terre trem-
bler sous leurs pas; la mer s'élève en bouillonnant dans
le port, et brise les vaisseaux qui sont à l'ancre.[1] Des
tourbillons de flammes et de cendres couvrent les rues
et les places publiques; les maisons s'écroulent, les
toits sont renversés sur les fondements, et les fonde-
ments se dispersent; trente mille habitants de tout âge
et de tout sexe sont écrasés sous des ruines. Le matelot
disait en sifflant et en jurant: "Il y aura quelque chose
à gagner ici. — Quelle peut être la raison suffisante de
ce phénomène? disait Pangloss. — Voici le dernier
jour du monde!" s'écriait Candide. Le matelot court
incontinent au milieu des débris, affronte la mort pour

[1] For the Lisbon Earthquake, see the Introduction.

for a moment and is engulfed forever. He wants to throw himself after him into the sea; the philosopher Pangloss prevents him, proving to him that the Lisbon roads had been expressly created that this Anabaptist might be drowned there. While he was proving this *a priori*, the vessel splits; everyone perishes except Pangloss, Candide, and that brutal sailor who had drowned the virtuous Anabaptist; the blackguard swam successfully to shore, to which Pangloss and Candide were carried on a plank.

When they had recovered a little, they walked toward Lisbon; they had some money left, with which they hoped to save themselves from starvation after they had escaped from the tempest.

Hardly have they set foot in the town, weeping over the death of their benefactor, when they feel the earth tremble under their feet, the sea rises up boiling in the harbor, and shatters the vessels at anchor.[1] Whirlwinds of flames and ashes cover the streets and public squares; houses crumble, roofs are toppling down on the foundations, and the foundations disintegrate; thirty thousand inhabitants of all ages and both sexes are crushed under the ruins. The sailor said, whistling and swearing: "There will be something to pick up here." — "What can be the sufficient reason of this phenomenon?" said Pangloss. — "Here's the last day of the world!" Candide exclaimed. The sailor runs immediately into the midst of the debris, braves death to find

trouver de l'argent, en trouve, s'en empare, s'enivre, et, ayant cuvé son vin, achète les faveurs de la première fille de bonne volonté qu'il rencontre sur les ruines des maisons détruites, et au milieu des mourants et des morts. Pangloss le tirait cependant par la manche. "Mon ami, lui disait-il, cela n'est pas bien, vous manquez à la raison universelle, vous prenez mal votre temps. — Tête et sang! répondit l'autre, je suis matelot et né à Batavia; j'ai marché quatre fois sur le crucifix dans quatre voyages au Japon;[2] tu as bien trouvé ton homme avec ta raison universelle!"

Quelques éclats de pierre avaient blessé Candide; il était étendu dans la rue et couvert de débris. Il disait à Pangloss: "Hélas! procure-moi un peu de vin et d'huile; je me meurs. — Ce tremblement de terre n'est pas une chose nouvelle, répondit Pangloss; la ville de Lima éprouva les mêmes secousses en Amérique l'année passée; mêmes causes, mêmes effets: il y a certainement une traînée de soufre sous terre depuis Lima jusqu'à Lisbonne. — Rien n'est plus probable, dit Candide; mais, pour Dieu, un peu d'huile et de vin. — Comment, probable? répliqua le philosophe; je soutiens que la chose est démontrée." Candide perdit connaissance et Pangloss lui apporta un peu d'eau d'une fontaine voisine.

Le lendemain, ayant trouvé quelques provisions de

[2] In his writings, Voltaire returns to this notion several times: he has Dutch merchants stamp on the cross before they are permitted to trade in Japan. But his possible source, Kaempfer's

money, finds some, grabs it, gets drunk, and when he has slept off his wine, buys the favors of the first girl of good will he meets on the ruins of destroyed houses, and in the midst of dying and dead. Meanwhile Pangloss took him by the sleeve and pulled him. "My friend," he said to him, "this is not good, you are failing universal reason, you are choosing your occasion badly." — "Hell and damn!" replied the other, "I am a sailor, born at Batavia; I have stepped on the crucifix four times in four voyages to Japan; [2] you have found the right man with your universal reason!"

Some splinters of stone had wounded Candide; he was stretched out in the street and covered with debris. He said to Pangloss: "Alas! Get me a little wine and oil; I am dying." — "This earthquake is not a new thing," replied Pangloss; "the city of Lima underwent the same shocks in America last year; same causes, same effects; there is certainly a vein of sulphur underground from Lima to Lisbon." — "Nothing is more probable," said Candide; "but, for God's sake, a little oil and wine." — "What do you mean, probable?" replied the philosopher, "I maintain that the matter is proved." Candide lost consciousness, and Pangloss brought him a little water from a neighboring fountain.

The next day, having found a little food as they

Histoire naturelle, civile et ecclésiastique de l'Empire du Japon (1729) merely reports that it was the *Japanese* working for the Dutch in Batavia who were compelled to perform this anti-Christian ceremony.

41

bouche en se glissant à travers des décombres, ils réparèrent un peu leurs forces. Ensuite ils travaillèrent comme les autres à soulager les habitants échappés à la mort. Quelques citoyens, secourus par eux, leur donnèrent un aussi bon dîner qu'on le pouvait dans un tel désastre: il est vrai que le repas était triste; les convives arrosaient leur pain de leurs larmes; mais Pangloss les consola en les assurant que les choses ne pouvaient être autrement: "Car, dit-il, tout ceci est ce qu'il y a de mieux: car, s'il y a un volcan à Lisbonne, il ne pouvait être ailleurs; car il est impossible que les choses ne soient pas où elles sont; car tout est bien."

Un petit homme noir, familier de l'Inquisition,[3] lequel était à côté de lui, prit poliment la parole et dit: "Apparemment que monsieur ne croit pas au péché originel: car, si tout est au mieux, il n'y a donc eu ni chute ni punition."

"Je demande très humblement pardon à Votre Excellence, répondit Pangloss encore plus poliment, car la chute de l'homme et la malédiction entraient nécessairement dans le meilleur des mondes possibles. — Monsieur ne croit donc pas à la liberté? dit le familier. — Votre Excellence m'excusera, dit Pangloss; la liberté peut subsister avec la nécessité absolue: car il était nécessaire que nous fussions libres; car enfin la volonté déterminée . . ." Pangloss était au milieu de sa phrase, quand le familier fit un signe de tête à son estafier qui lui servait à boire du vin de Porto ou d'Oporto.

[3] *"Familier"* is the title of the officer of the Inquisition whose task it is to arrest accused persons.

crept through the debris, they restored their strength a little. Later they worked like the others to relieve the inhabitants who had escaped death. Some citizens, whom they had helped, gave them as good a dinner as they could in such a disaster; it is true that the meal was sad; the guests watered their bread with their tears; but Pangloss consoled them by assuring them that things could not be otherwise. "For," he said, "all this is for the best; for if there is a volcano in Lisbon, it could not be elsewhere; for it is impossible that things are not where they are; for all is well."

A short dark man, a Familiar of the Inquisition,[3] who was by his side, politely took the floor and said: "Apparently the gentleman does not believe in original sin; for if everything is for the best, then there was neither fall nor punishment."

"I very humbly beg your excellency's pardon," replied Pangloss still more politely, "for the fall of man and the curse necessarily entered into the best of possible worlds." — "Then Monsieur does not believe in free will?" said the official. — "Your excellency will excuse me," said Pangloss; "free will can exist with absolute necessity, for it was necessary that we are free; for after all, determined will . . ." Pangloss was in the middle of his sentence, when the Familiar gave a signal with his head to his flunky, who was pouring him some wine from Porto or Oporto.

Chapitre Sixième

Comment on Fit un Bel Auto-da-Fé Pour Empêcher les Tremblements de Terre, et Comment Candide Fut Fessé

Après le tremblement de terre qui avait détruit les trois quarts de Lisbonne, les sages du pays n'avaient pas trouvé un moyen plus efficace pour prévenir une ruine totale que de donner au peuple un bel auto-da-fé; [1] il était décidé par l'université de Coïmbre que le spectacle de quelques personnes brûlées à petit feu, en grande cérémonie, est un secret infaillible pour empêcher la terre de trembler.

On avait en conséquence saisi un Biscayen convaincu d'avoir épousé sa commère, et deux Portugais qui en mangeant un poulet en avaient arraché le lard: [2] on vint lier après le dîner le docteur Pangloss et son di-

[1] From the Portuguese, meaning "act of faith"; the sentence of the Inquisition, or, more commonly, the public carrying out of that sentence, such as the burning of a heretic. There actually were several *auto-da-fés* in Lisbon from 1756 to 1758, but they had nothing to do with the earthquake, and were not as ferocious as Voltaire pictures them.

Sixth Chapter

How They Held a Splendid Auto-da-Fé to Prevent Earthquakes, and How Candide Was Flogged

After the earthquake which had destroyed three-quarters of Lisbon, the sages of the country had not found a more efficacious means of preventing total ruin than to give the people a splendid auto-da-fé; [1] it was decided by the University of Coimbre that the spectacle of a few persons burned on a slow fire in a great ceremony is an infallible secret for preventing the earth from quaking.

Consequently they had seized a Biscayan convicted of having married his godmother, and two Portuguese who had thrown away the bacon before eating the chicken; [2] after dinner they came to tie up Doctor

[2] That is to say, who were secretly Jews. For centuries, the Spanish and Portuguese Inquisitions had been on the lookout for those *marranos* (that is, Spanish or Portuguese Jews converted to Christianity) who practiced their old religion in private. Voltaire, who was prejudiced against Jews, nevertheless pitied the many Jewish victims of the Inquisition.

sciple Candide, l'un pour avoir parlé, et l'autre pour avoir écouté avec un air d'approbation: tous deux furent menés séparément dans des appartements d'une extrême fraîcheur, dans lesquels on n'était jamais incommodé du soleil: huit jours après ils furent tous deux revêtus d'un san-benito,[3] et on orna leurs têtes de mitres de papier: la mitre et le san-benito de Candide étaient peints de flammes renversées et de diables qui n'avaient ni queues ni griffes; mais les diables de Pangloss portaient griffes et queues, et les flammes étaient droites. Ils marchèrent en procession ainsi vêtus, et entendirent un sermon très pathétique, suivi d'une belle musique en faux-bourdon. Candide fut fessé en cadence, pendant qu'on chantait; le Biscayen et les deux hommes qui n'avaient point voulu manger de lard furent brûlés, et Pangloss fut pendu, quoique ce ne soit pas la coutume. Le même jour, la terre trembla de nouveau avec un fracas épouvantable.[4]

Candide, épouvanté, interdit, éperdu, tout sanglant, tout palpitant, se disait à lui-même: "Si c'est ici le meilleur des mondes possibles, que sont donc les autres? Passe encore si je n'étais que fessé, je l'ai été chez les Bulgares; mais, ô mon cher Pangloss! le plus grand des philosophes, faut-il vous avoir vu pendre sans que je sache pourquoi! O mon cher anabaptiste! le meilleur des hommes, faut-il que vous ayez été noyé

[3] A yellow penitential garment worn by a confessed heretic, especially before being burned at the stake. Voltaire's detailed descriptions—including the devils painted on the mitres of Candide and Pangloss—are taken from contemporary accounts.

Pangloss and his disciple Candide, one for having spoken, and the other for having listened with an air of approval; both of them were led separately into apartments of extreme coldness, in which one was never bothered by the sun; a week later both of them were dressed in a *sanbenito*,[3] and their heads were decorated with paper mitres; Candide's mitre and *sanbenito* were painted with upside down flames, and with devils which had neither tails nor claws; but Pangloss's devils wore claws and tails, and the flames were right side up. Later, they marched in procession, and listened to a highly pathetic sermon, followed by some beautiful music in plain song. During the singing Candide was flogged in cadence; the Biscayan and the two men who had not wanted to eat bacon were burned, and Pangloss was hanged even though this was not the custom. On the same day the earth quaked once more, with a terrifying din.[4]

Candide, terrified, stupefied, bewildered, all bleeding, all quivering, said to himself: "If this is the best of possible worlds, what then are the others? Had I only been flogged, well, I could let that pass, the Bulgarians flogged me too; but O my dear Pangloss! the greatest of philosophers, was it necessary to see you hanged without my knowing why! O my dear Anabaptist! the best of men, was it necessary for you to

[4] Actually, this second earthquake took place almost two months after the first, on 21 December 1755. As Voltaire notes in his correspondence, it was much less destructive, killing fewer than a hundred persons.

dans le port! O mademoiselle Cunégonde! la perle des filles, faut-il qu'on vous ait fendu le ventre!"

Il s'en retournait se soutenant à peine, prêché, fessé, absous et béni, lorsqu'une vieille l'aborda et lui dit: "Mon fils, prenez courage, suivez-moi."

be drowned in the harbor! O Mademoiselle Cunégonde! the pearl of young ladies, was it necessary for your belly to be cut open!"

He turned away barely standing up, preached at, flogged, absolved and blessed, when an old woman accosted him, and said to him: "My son, take courage, follow me."

Chapitre Septième

Comment une Vieille Prit Soin de Candide, et
Comment Il Retrouva ce Qu'Il Aimait

Candide ne prit point courage, mais il suivit la vieille
dans une masure: elle lui donna un pot de pommade
pour se frotter, lui laissa à manger et à boire; elle lui
montra un petit lit assez propre; il y avait auprès du
lit un habit complet. "Mangez, buvez, dormez, lui
dit-elle, et que Notre-Dame d'Atocha,[1] monseigneur
saint Antoine de Padoue et monseigneur saint Jacques
de Compostelle prennent soin de vous: je reviendrai
demain." Candide, toujours étonné de tout ce qu'il
avait vu, de tout ce qu'il avait souffert, et encore plus
de la charité de la vieille, voulut lui baiser la main.
"Ce n'est pas ma main qu'il faut baiser, dit la vieille;
je reviendrai demain. Frottez-vous de pommade, man-
gez et dormez."

Candide, malgré tant de malheurs, mangea et dormit.
Le lendemain la vieille lui apporte à déjeuner, visite

[1] Voltaire refers to this miraculous wooden statue of the
Virgin in his early version of *Candide*, the *Histoire des voyages*

Seventh Chapter

How an Old Woman Took Care of Candide, and How He Recovered What He Loved

Candide did not take courage, but he followed the old woman into a hovel; she gave him a jar of ointment to rub himself with, left him food and drink; she showed him a fairly clean bed; beside the bed there was a complete set of clothes. "Eat, drink, sleep," she said to him, "and may Our Lady of Atocha,[1] Monseigneur Saint Anthony of Padua and Monseigneur Saint James of Compostella take care of you! I shall return tomorrow." Candide, still astonished at everything he had seen, at everything he had suffered, and still more at the old woman's charity, wanted to kiss her hand. "It's not my hand you should kiss," said the old woman. "I shall come back tomorrow. Rub yourself with the ointment, eat and sleep."

Candide, despite so many misfortunes, ate and slept. The next day, the old woman brings him some breakfast, examines his back, rubs it herself with another

de Scarmentado (see *Oeuvres*, xxi, 127–8). This statue, in Madrid, supposedly wept annually on its feast day.

son dos, le frotte elle-même d'une autre pommade; elle lui apporte ensuite à dîner; elle revient sur le soir, et apporte à souper. Le surlendemain, elle fit encore les mêmes cérémonies. "Qui êtes-vous? lui disait toujours Candide; qui vous a inspiré tant de bonté? quelles grâces puis-je vous rendre?" La bonne femme ne répondait jamais rien: elle revint sur le soir et n'apporta point à souper. "Venez avec moi, dit-elle, et ne dites mot." Elle le prend sous le bras, et marche avec lui dans la campagne environ un quart de mille: ils arrivent à une maison isolée, entourée de jardins et de canaux. La vieille frappe à une petite porte. On ouvre; elle mène Candide, par un escalier dérobé, dans un cabinet doré, le laisse sur un canapé de brocart, referme la porte, et s'en va. Candide croyait rêver, et regardait toute sa vie comme un songe funeste, et le moment présent comme un songe agréable.

La vieille reparut bientôt; elle soutenait avec peine une femme tremblante, d'une taille majestueuse, brillante de pierreries, et couverte d'un voile. "Otez ce voile," dit la vieille à Candide. Le jeune homme approche; il lève le voile d'une main timide. Quel moment! quelle surprise! il croit voir Mademoiselle Cunégonde; il la voyait en effet, c'était elle-même. La force lui manque, il ne peut proférer une parole, il tombe à ses pieds. Cunégonde tombe sur le canapé. La vieille les accable d'eaux spiritueuses; ils reprennent leurs sens, ils se parlent: ce sont d'abord des mots entrecoupés, des demandes et des réponses qui se croisent, des sou-

ointment; later she brings him dinner; she returns toward evening and brings supper. The next day, she continued to perform the same ceremonies. "Who are you?" Candide kept asking her; "who has inspired you with so much goodness? What thanks can I return?" The good woman never answered anything; she came back toward evening, and did not bring supper. "Come with me," she said, "and don't say a word." She takes him by the arm, and walks with him in the countryside for about a quarter of a mile; they arrive at an isolated house, surrounded by gardens and canals. The old woman knocks at the little door. Someone opens the door; she leads Candide, by a hidden staircase, into a gilded boudoir and leaves him on a brocaded sofa, closes the door again, and departs. Candide thought he was dreaming, and thought of his whole life as a sinister dream, and the present moment as an agreeable dream.

The old woman soon reappeared; with difficulty she was supporting a trembling woman of majestic height, glittering with precious stones, and covered with a veil. "Remove that veil," said the old woman to Candide. The young man approaches; he raises the veil with a timid hand. What a moment! What a surprise! He thinks he is seeing Mademoiselle Cunégonde; he actually saw her, it was she herself. Strength fails him, he cannot utter a word, he falls at her feet. Cunégonde falls onto the sofa. The old woman pours scents all over them, they regain their senses, they speak to each other; at first they are only disconnected words, questions and replies crossing one another, sighs,

pirs, des larmes, des cris.[2] La vieille leur recommande
de faire moins de bruit, et les laisse en liberté. "Quoi!
c'est vous, lui dit Candide, vous vivez, je vous retrouve
en Portugal! On ne vous a donc pas violée? On ne
vous a point fendu le ventre, comme le philosophe
Pangloss me l'avait assuré? — Si fait, dit la belle Cuné-
gonde; mais on ne meurt pas toujours de ces deux
accidents. — Mais votre père et votre mère ont-ils
été tués? — Il n'est que trop vrai, dit Cunégonde en
pleurant. — Et votre frère? — Mon frère a été tué
aussi. — Et pourquoi êtes-vous en Portugal? et com-
ment avez-vous su que j'y étais? et par quelle étrange
aventure m'avez-vous fait conduire dans cette maison?
— Je vous dirai tout cela, répliqua la dame; mais il faut
auparavant que vous m'appreniez tout ce qui vous est
arrivé depuis le baiser innocent que vous me donnâtes
et les coups de pied que vous reçûtes."

Candide lui obéit avec un profond respect; et, quoi-
qu'il fût interdit, quoique sa voix fût faible et trem-
blante, quoique l'échine lui fît encore un peu mal, il
lui raconta de la manière la plus naïve tout ce qu'il
avait éprouvé depuis le moment de leur séparation.
Cunégonde levait les yeux au ciel: elle donna des
larmes à la mort du bon anabaptiste et de Pangloss;
après quoi elle parla en ces termes à Candide, qui ne
perdait pas une parole, et qui la dévorait des yeux.

[2] Readers of sentimental eighteenth-century novels must have
been much amused by this, and the other recognition scenes
with which Voltaire parodies the fashions of his time.

tears, cries.[2] The old woman recommends that they make less noise, and leaves them to themselves. "What! It's you," Candide says to her; "you're alive! I find you again in Portugal! Then you were not raped? They did not slit your belly, as the philosopher Pangloss had assured me?" — "Yes, it happened," said the beautiful Cunégonde; "but one doesn't always die from these two accidents." — "But were your father and your mother killed?" — "That's only too true," said Cunégonde weeping. — "And your brother?" — "My brother too was killed." — "And why are you in Portugal? And how did you find out that I was here and through what strange adventure did you have me brought to this house?" — "I'll tell you all that," replied the lady. "Before that you must tell me everything that happened to you since the innocent kiss you gave me and the kicks that you received."

Candide obeyed her with profound respect; and even though he was stupefied, even though his voice was weak and trembling, even though his spine still gave him a little pain, he told her in the most naive way everything he had undergone from the moment of their separation. Cunégonde raised her eyes to heaven; she shed tears at the death of the good Anabaptist and of Pangloss; afterwards she spoke in these terms to Candide, who did not miss a word, and devoured her with his eyes.

Chapitre Huitième

Histoire de Cunégonde

"J'étais dans mon lit et je dormais profondément, quand il plut au Ciel d'envoyer les Bulgares dans notre beau château de Thunder-ten-tronckh; ils égorgèrent mon père et mon frère, et coupèrent ma mère par morceaux. Un grand Bulgare, haut de six pieds, voyant qu'à ce spectacle j'avais perdu connaissance, se mit à me violer; cela me fit revenir, je repris mes sens, je criai, je me débattis, je mordis, j'égratignai, je voulais arracher les yeux à ce grand Bulgare, ne sachant pas que tout ce qui arrivait dans le château de mon père était chose d'usage: le brutal me donna un coup de couteau dans le flanc gauche dont je porte encore la marque. — Hélas! j'espère bien la voir, dit le naïf Candide. — Vous la verrez, dit Cunégonde; mais continuons. — Continuez," dit Candide.

Elle reprit ainsi le fil de son histoire: "Un capitaine bulgare entra, il me vit toute sanglante, et le soldat ne se dérangeait pas. Le capitaine se mit en colère du peu de respect que lui témoignait ce brutal, et le tua sur mon corps. Ensuite il me fit panser, et m'emmena

Eighth Chapter

Cunégonde's Story

"I was in my bed and I was sleeping deeply, when it pleased heaven to send the Bulgarians to our handsome country house of Thunder-ten-trockh; they butchered my father and my brother, and cut my mother into pieces. A big Bulgarian, six feet tall, seeing that I had lost consciousness at this spectacle, got ready to rape me; that brought me around, I recovered my senses, I screamed, I struggled, I bit, I scratched, I tried to tear that big Bulgarian's eyes out, not knowing that everything that was happening in my father's country house was a matter of custom; the brute stabbed me with a knife in the left side where I still bear the mark." — "Alas! I certainly hope to see it," said the naive Candide. — "You'll see it," said Cunégonde; "but let us go on." — "Go on," said Candide.

She took up the thread of her story as follows: "A Bulgarian captain entered, he saw me all bleeding, and the soldier was in no way disturbed. The captain got angry at the little respect this brute showed him, and killed him on my body. Then he had me bandaged,

prisonnière de guerre dans son quartier. Je blanchissais le peu de chemises qu'il avait, je faisais sa cuisine; il me trouvait fort jolie, il faut l'avouer; et je ne nierai pas qu'il ne fût très bien fait, et qu'il n'eût la peau blanche et douce; d'ailleurs peu d'esprit, peu de philosophie: on voyait bien qu'il n'avait pas été élevé par le docteur Pangloss. Au bout de trois mois, ayant perdu tout son argent et s'étant dégoûté de moi, il me vendit à un juif nommé don Issachar, qui trafiquait en Hollande et en Portugal, et qui aimait passionnément les femmes. Ce juif s'attacha beaucoup à ma personne, mais il ne pouvait en triompher; je lui ai mieux résisté qu'au soldat bulgare: une personne d'honneur peut être violée une fois, mais sa vertu s'en affermit. Le juif, pour m'apprivoiser, me mena dans cette maison de campagne que vous voyez. J'avais cru jusque là qu'il n'y avait rien sur la terre de si beau que le château de Thunder-ten-tronckh; j'ai été détrompée.

"Le grand inquisiteur m'aperçut un jour à la messe; il me lorgna beaucoup, et me fit dire qu'il avait à me parler pour des affaires secrètes. Je fus conduite à son palais; je lui appris ma naissance; il me représenta combien il était au-dessous de mon rang d'appartenir à un israélite. On proposa de sa part à don Issachar de me céder à monseigneur. Don Issachar, qui est le banquier de la cour et homme de crédit, n'en voulut rien faire. L'inquisiteur le menaça d'un auto-da-fé. Enfin mon juif, intimidé, conclut un marché par lequel la maison et moi leur appartiendraient à tous deux en

and brought me to his quarters as a prisoner of war. I washed the few shirts he had, I cooked for him; he found me very pretty, I must admit; and I won't deny that he was very well built, and that he had white and soft skin; on the other hand little wit and little philosophy; it was easy to see that he had not been educated by Doctor Pangloss. At the end of three months, having lost all his money, and being tired of me, he sold me to a Jew named Don Issachar, who traded in Holland and Portugal, and who loved women passionately. This Jew became much attached to my person, but he could not triumph over it; I resisted him better than the Bulgarian soldier; a person of honor may be raped once, but her virtue grows stronger from that. The Jew, in order to tame me, brought me into this country house that you see. Until then I had thought there was nothing in the world so handsome as the country house at Thunder-ten-trockh; I was undeceived.

"The Grand Inquisitor noticed me one day at Mass; he leered at me a good deal, and sent word to me that he had to speak to me about secret matters. I was taken to his palace; I informed him of my birth, he pointed out to me how much beneath my rank it was to belong to an Israelite. It was proposed on his behalf that Don Issachar give me up to Monseigneur. Don Issachar, who is the court banker, and a man of influence, would do no such thing. The Inquisitor threatened him with an auto-da-fé. Finally, my Jew, intimidated, concluded a bargain by which the house and I would belong to both of them in common; that

commun; que le juif aurait pour lui les lundis, mercredis et le jour du sabbat, et que l'inquisiteur aurait les autres jours de la semaine. Il y a six mois que cette convention subsiste. Ce n'a pas été sans querelles: car souvent il a été indécis si la nuit du samedi au dimanche appartenait à l'ancienne loi ou à la nouvelle. Pour moi, j'ai résisté jusqu'à présent à toutes les deux; et je crois que c'est pour cette raison que j'ai toujours été aimée.

"Enfin, pour détourner le fléau des tremblements de terre et pour intimider don Issachar, il plut à monseigneur l'inquisiteur de célébrer un auto-da-fé. Il me fit l'honneur de m'y inviter. Je fus très bien placée; on servit aux dames des rafraîchissements entre la messe et l'exécution. Je fus, à la vérité, saisie d'horreur en voyant brûler ces deux juifs et cet honnête Biscayen qui avait épousé sa commère; mais quelle fut ma surprise, mon effroi, mon trouble, quand je vis, dans un san-benito et sous une mitre, une figure qui ressemblait à celle de Pangloss! Je me frottai les yeux, je regardai attentivement, je le vis pendre; je tombai en faiblesse. A peine reprenais-je mes sens que je vous vis dépouillé tout nu: ce fut là le comble de l'horreur, de la consternation, de la douleur, du désespoir. Je vous dirai, avec vérité, que votre peau est encore plus blanche et d'un incarnat plus parfait que celle de mon capitaine des Bulgares. Cette vue redoubla tous les sentiments qui m'accablaient, qui me dévoraient. Je m'écriai, je voulus dire: 'Arrêtez, barbares!' mais la voix me manqua, et mes cris auraient été inutiles. Quand vous eûtes été

the Jew would have Mondays, Wednesdays, and the Sabbath day for him, and the Inquisitor would have the other days of the week. This treaty has lasted for six months. It has not been without quarrels; for often it has been undecided whether the night from Saturday to Sunday belonged to the old law or the new. As for myself, I have resisted both of them up to now; and I think that it is for this reason that I have continued to be loved.

"Finally, to turn away the scourge of earthquakes, and to intimidate Don Issachar, it pleased Monseigneur the Inquisitor to celebrate an auto-da-fé. He did me the honor of inviting me to it. I had a very good seat; they served refreshments ·to the ladies between the Mass and the execution. In truth, I was seized with horror when I saw those two Jews and that honest Biscayan who had married his godmother being burned; but imagine my surprise, my fright, my distress, when I saw, in a *sanbenito* and under a mitre, the face resembling that of Pangloss! I rubbed my eyes, I looked attentively, I saw him hanged; I fell into a faint. I had hardly recovered my senses when I saw you stripped stark naked; that was the height of horror, of consternation, of pain, of despair. I will tell you truthfully, that your skin is even whiter and of a more perfect flesh color than that of my captain of Bulgarians. This sight redoubled all the feelings that overwhelmed me, that devoured me. I cried out, I wanted to say: 'Stop, Barbarians!' but my voice failed me, and my cries would have been useless. When you had been

bien fessé: 'Comment se peut-il faire, disais-je, que l'aimable Candide et le sage Pangloss se trouvent à Lisbonne, l'un pour recevoir cent coups de fouet, et l'autre pour être pendu par l'ordre de monseigneur l'inquisiteur, dont je suis la bien-aimée? Pangloss m'a donc bien cruellement trompée quand il me disait que tout va le mieux du monde.'

"Agitée, éperdue, tantôt hors de moi-même, et tantôt prête de mourir de faiblesse, j'avais la tête remplie du massacre de mon père, de ma mère, de mon frère, de l'insolence de mon vilain soldat bulgare, du coup de couteau qu'il me donna, de ma servitude, de mon métier de cuisinière, de mon capitaine bulgare, de mon vilain don Issachar, de mon abominable inquisiteur, de la pendaison du docteur Pangloss, de ce grand *miserere*[1] en faux-bourdon pendant lequel on vous fessait, et surtout du baiser que je vous avais donné derrière un paravent, le jour que je vous avais vu pour la dernière fois. Je louai Dieu, qui vous ramenait à moi par tant d'épreuves. Je recommandai à ma vieille d'avoir soin de vous, et de vous amener ici dès qu'elle le pourrait. Elle a très bien exécuté ma commission; j'ai goûté le plaisir inexprimable de vous revoir, de vous entendre, de vous parler. Vous devez avoir une faim dévorante; j'ai grand appétit; commençons par souper."

[1] Latin chant based on the opening of the fifty-first psalm: "Have mercy upon me, O God . . ."

thoroughly flogged, I said: 'How can it be, that the pleasant Candide and the wise Pangloss should be in Lisbon, one to receive a hundred strokes, and the other to be hanged by order of Monseigneur the Inquisitor, whose dearly beloved I am? Pangloss, then, most cruelly deceived me when he told me that all is for the very best.'

"Agitated, bewildered, sometimes beside myself and sometimes ready to die of faintness, I had my mind full of the massacre of my father, of my mother, of my brother, the insolence of my vile Bulgarian soldier, of the knife cut he gave me, of my slavery, of my trade as cook, of my Bulgarian captain, of my vile Don Issachar, of my abominable Inquisitor, of the hanging of Doctor Pangloss, of that great *miserere* [1] in plain song while you were being whipped, and above all of the kiss I had given you behind the screen the day I had seen you for the last time. I praised God, who was leading you back to me through so many trials. I ordered my old woman to take care of you, and to bring you here as quickly as she could. She has carried out my commission very well; I have tasted the inexpressible pleasure of seeing you again, of hearing you, of speaking to you. You must be ravenously hungry; I have a good appetite; let's begin with supper."

Les voilà qui se mettent tous deux à table; et, après
le souper, ils se replacent sur ce beau canapé dont on
a déjà parlé; ils y étaient quand le signor don Issachar,
l'un des maîtres de la maison, arriva. C'était le jour du
sabbat. Il venait jouir de ses droits, et expliquer son
tendre amour.

Here they are both of them sitting down to supper; and after supper they resume their places on the handsome sofa that has already been mentioned; they were there when Monseigneur Don Issachar, one of the masters of the house, arrived. It was the day of the Sabbath. He was coming to enjoy his rights and explain his tender love.

Chapitre Neuvième

Ce Qui Advint de Cunégonde, de Candide, du Grand Inquisiteur, et d'un Juif

Cet Issachar était le plus colérique Hébreu qu'on eût vu dans Israël, depuis la captivité en Babylone. "Quoi! dit-il, chienne de galiléenne, ce n'est pas assez de monsieur l'inquisiteur? Il faut que ce coquin partage aussi avec moi?" En disant cela il tire un long poignard dont il était toujours pourvu, et, ne croyant pas que son adverse partie eût des armes, il se jette sur Candide; mais notre bon Vestphalien avait reçu une belle épée de la vieille avec l'habit complet. Il tire son épée, quoiqu'il eût les mœurs fort douces, et vous étend l'israélite roide mort sur le carreau, aux pieds de la belle Cunégonde.

"Sainte Vierge! s'écria-t-elle, qu'allons-nous devenir? Un homme tué chez moi! si la justice vient, nous sommes perdus. — Si Pangloss n'avait pas été pendu, dit Candide, il nous donnerait un bon conseil dans cette extrémité, car c'était un grand philosophe. A son défaut consultons la vieille." Elle était fort prudente, et commençait à dire son avis, quand une autre petite

Ninth Chapter

What Happened to Cunégonde, Candide, the Grand Inquisitor, and a Jew

This Issachar was the most choleric Hebrew ever seen in Israel since the Babylonian captivity. "What!" he said, "Bitch of a Galilean, isn't Monsieur the Inquisitor enough? Must this rascal share with me too?" Saying this, he draws a long dagger which he had always on him, and, not thinking that his adversary was armed, throws himself on Candide; but our good Westphalian had received a fine sword from the old woman together with the set of clothes. He draws the sword, even though he had the gentlest of characters, and stretches the Israelite out on the floor stone dead, at the feet of the beautiful Cunégonde.

"Holy Virgin!" she exclaimed, "what is to become of us? A man killed in my house! If the police comes, we are lost." — "If Pangloss had not been hanged," said Candide, "he would give us a good piece of advice in this extremity, for he was a great philosopher. Since he's not here, let's consult the old woman." She was extremely prudent, and was beginning to give her advice when another little door opened. It was an hour

porte s'ouvrit. Il était une heure après minuit, cétait le commencement du dimanche. Ce jour appartenait à monseigneur l'inquisiteur. Il entre et voit le fessé Candide l'épée à la main, un mort étendu par terre, Cunégonde effarée, et la vieille donnant des conseils.

Voici dans ce moment ce qui se passa dans l'âme de Candide, et comment il raisonna: "Si ce saint homme appelle du secours, il me fera infailliblement brûler; il pourra en faire autant de Cunégonde; il m'a fait fouetter impitoyablement; il est mon rival; je suis en train de tuer, il n'y a pas à balancer." Ce raisonnement fut net et rapide; et, sans donner le temps à l'inquisiteur de revenir de sa surprise, il le perce d'outre en outre, et le jette à côté du juif. "En voici bien d'une autre, dit Cunégonde; il n'y a plus de rémission; nous sommes excommuniés, notre dernière heure est venue. Comment avez-vous fait, vous qui êtes né si doux, pour tuer en deux minutes un juif et un prélat? — Ma belle demoiselle, répondit Candide, quand on est amoureux, jaloux et fouetté par l'Inquisition, on ne se connaît plus."

La vieille prit alors la parole et dit: "Il y a trois chevaux andalous dans l'écurie, avec leurs selles et leurs brides: que le brave Candide les prépare; madame a des moyadors[1] et des diamants: montons vite à cheval, quoique je ne puisse me tenir que sur une fesse, et allons à Cadix; il fait le plus beau temps du monde, et c'est un grand plaisir de voyager pendant la fraîcheur de la nuit."

[1] An old Portuguese gold coin.

after midnight, it was the beginning of Sunday. This day belonged to Monseigneur the Inquisitor. He comes in and sees the flogged Candide, sword in hand, a dead man stretched on the ground, Cunégonde scared, and the old woman giving advice.

Here is what went on at this moment in Candide's soul and how he reasoned: "If this holy man calls for help, he will have me burned without fail, he could do the same to Cunégonde; he has had me flogged pitilessly; he is my rival; I am in the course of killing; there is no hesitating." This reasoning was clear and rapid; and, without giving the Inquisitor time to recover from his surprise, he pierces him through and through, and throws him beside the Jew. "Well, here's another one," said Cunégonde; "there will be no more mercy; we are excommunicated, our last hour has come! What happened to you, you who were born so gentle, to kill a Jew and a prelate in two minutes?" — "My fair lady," replied Candide, "when you are in love, jealous, and whipped by the Inquisition, you are beside yourself."

The old woman then spoke up and said: "There are three Andalusian horses in the stable, with their saddles and bridles; let the brave Candide get them ready; Madame has moidores [1] and diamonds, let us mount quickly, although I cannot ride on more than one buttock, and let's go to Cadiz; the weather is the best in the world, and it's a great pleasure to travel during the cool of the night."

Aussitôt Candide selle les trois chevaux. Cunégonde, la vieille, et lui, font trente milles d'une traite. Pendant qu'ils s'éloignaient, la Ste. Hermandad [2] arrive dans la maison; on enterre monseigneur dans une belle église, et on jette Issachar à la voirie.

Candide, Cunégonde, et la vieille, étaient déjà dans la petite ville d'Avacéna, au milieu des montagnes de la Sierra-Morena; et ils parlaient ainsi dans un cabaret.

[2] The *Ste. Hermandad* was a Spanish "brotherhood," founded about the sixteenth century for the purpose of pursuing criminals.

Candide saddled the three horses right away. Cuné-
gonde, the old woman, and he rode thirty miles in
one stretch. While they are going off, the Holy
Brotherhood [2] arrives in the house, and they bury
Monseigneur in a beautiful church and throw Issachar
into the gutter.

Candide, Cunégonde, and the old woman were al-
ready in the little town of Avacena in the middle
of the mountains of the Sierra Morena; and this is
how they talked in an inn.

Chapitre Dixième

Dans Quelle Détresse Candide, Cunégonde et la Vieille Arrivent à Cadix, et de Leur Embarquement

"Qui a donc pu me voler mes pistoles [1] et mes diamants? disait en pleurant Cunégonde; de quoi vivrons-nous? comment ferons-nous? où trouver des inquisiteurs et des juifs qui m'en donnent d'autres? — Hélas! dit la vieille, je soupçonne fort un révérend père cordelier qui coucha hier dans la même auberge que nous à Badajos; Dieu me garde de faire un jugement téméraire! mais il entra deux fois dans notre chambre, et il partit longtemps avant nous. — Hélas! dit Candide, le bon Pangloss m'avait souvent prouvé que les biens de la terre sont communs à tous les hommes, que chacun y a un droit égal. Ce cordelier devait bien, suivant ces principes, nous laisser de quoi achever notre voyage. Il ne vous reste donc rien du tout, ma belle Cunégonde? — Pas un maravédis,[2] dit-elle. — Quel

[1] A Spanish gold coin.
[2] A Spanish copper coin of small value.

Tenth Chapter

In What Distress Candide, Cunégonde, and the Old Woman Arrive at Cadiz, and about Their Embarkation

"Now who could have stolen my pistoles [1] and my diamonds?" said Cunégonde crying; "what shall we live on? What shall we do? Where will we find Inquisitors and Jews who will give me others?" — "Alas!" said the old woman, "I strongly suspect a reverend Franciscan father who slept in the same inn we did yesterday at Badajoz; God preserve me from making a rash judgment! But he came into our room twice and he left long before we did." — "Alas!" said Candide, "the good Pangloss had often proved to me that the goods things of the earth are common to all men, that everyone has the same right to them. This Franciscan, according to these principles, should have left us enough to complete our voyage. You've got nothing left, then, my beautiful Cunégonde?" — "Not a maravedi," [2] she said. — "What are we to do?" said

parti prendre? dit Candide. — Vendons un des chevaux, dit la vieille; je monterai en croupe derrière mademoiselle, quoique je ne puisse me tenir que sur une fesse, et nous arriverons à Cadix."

Il y avait dans la même hôtellerie un prieur de bénédictins; il acheta le cheval bon marché. Candide, Cunégonde, et la vieille passèrent par Lucena, par Chillas, par Lebrixa, et arrivèrent enfin à Cadix.[3] On y équipait une flotte, et on y assemblait des troupes pour mettre à la raison les révérends pères jésuites du Paraguai, qu'on accusait d'avoir fait révolter une de leurs hordes contre les rois d'Espagne et de Portugal, auprès de la ville du Saint Sacrement.[4] Candide, ayant servi chez les Bulgares, fit l'exercice bulgarien devant le général de la petite armée avec tant de grâce, de célérité, d'adresse, de fierté, d'agilité, qu'on lui donna une compagnie d'infanterie à commander. Le voilà capitaine; il s'embarque avec Mademoiselle Cunégonde, la vieille, deux valets, et les deux chevaux andalous qui avaient appartenu à monsieur le grand inquisiteur de Portugal.

Pendant toute la traversée ils raisonnèrent beaucoup sur la philosophie du pauvre Pangloss. "Nous allons dans un autre univers, disait Candide; c'est dans celui-là sans doute que tout est bien: car il faut avouer qu'on pourrait gémir un peu de ce qui se passe dans le nôtre

[3] Hardly a realistic itinerary, as André Morize pointed out: while Lucena, Lebrixa, and Cadiz are in Spain, Chillas is a small town near Lisbon.

[4] This "rebellion" actually took place from 1754 to 1756, in consequence of an exchange of territory between Spain and Por-

Candide. — "Let's sell one of the horses," said the old woman; "I'll ride on the rump behind Mademoiselle, although I can sit on only one buttock, and we'll get to Cadiz."

In the same hostelry there was a Benedictine prior; he bought the horse at a bargain. Candide, Cunégonde, and the old woman passed through Lucena, Chillas, Lebrixa, and finally arrived at Cadiz.[3] A fleet was being outfitted there, and they were assembling troops to bring to reason the reverend Jesuit fathers of Paraguay who were accused of causing the revolt of one of their tribes against the kings of Spain and Portugal near the town of Sacramento.[4] Candide, having served with the Bulgarians, performed the Bulgarian drill before the general of the new army with such grace, speed, skill, pride, agility, that they gave him an infantry company to command. There he is, captain; he embarks with Mademoiselle Cunégonde, the old woman, two valets, and the two Andalusian horses that had belonged to Monsieur the Grand Inquisitor of Portugal.

During the whole crossing they argued a great deal about the philosophy of poor Pangloss. "We are going to another universe," said Candide; "doubtless, in that one all is well. For it must be admitted that one might deplore a little what goes on in ours in the

tugal. Voltaire believed that the Jesuits in Paraguay had objected to cessions of territory to Portugal and had actually stirred up the Indians, but this is doubtful.

en physique et en morale. — Je vous aime de tout mon cœur, disait Cunégonde; mais j'ai encore l'âme tout effarouchée de ce que j'ai vu, de ce que j'ai éprouvé. — Tout ira bien, répliquait Candide; la mer de ce nouveau monde vaut déjà mieux que les mers de notre Europe; elle est plus calme, les vents plus constants. C'est certainement le nouveau monde qui est le meilleur des univers possibles. — Dieu le veuille! disait Cunégonde; mais j'ai été si horriblement malheureuse dans le mien que mon cœur est presque fermé à l'espérance. — Vous vous plaignez, leur dit la vieille; hélas! vous n'avez pas éprouvé des infortunes telles que les miennes." Cunégonde se mit presque à rire, et trouva cette bonne femme fort plaisante de prétendre être plus malheureuse qu'elle. "Hélas! lui dit-elle, ma bonne, à moins que vous n'ayez été violée par deux Bulgares, que vous n'ayez reçu deux coups de couteau dans le ventre, qu'on n'ait démoli deux de vos châteaux, qu'on n'ait égorgé à vos yeux deux mères et deux pères, et que nous n'ayez vu deux de vos amants fouettés dans un auto-da-fé, je ne vois pas que vous puissiez l'emporter sur moi; ajoutez que je suis née baronne avec soixante et douze quartiers, et que j'ai été cuisinière. — Mademoiselle, répondit la vieille, vous ne savez pas quelle est ma naissance; et si je vous montrais mon derrière, vous ne parleriez pas comme vous faites, et vous suspendriez votre jugement." Ce discours fit naître une extrême curiosité dans l'esprit de Cunégonde et de Candide. La vieille leur parla en ces termes.

physical and moral realms." — "I love you with all my heart," said Cunégonde, "but my soul is still terrified by what I have seen, by what I have undergone." — "All will be well," replied Candide; "the sea of this new world is already worth more than the seas of our Europe; it is calmer and the winds are more constant. It's surely the new world which is the best of possible universes." — "God grant it!" said Cunégonde; "but I have been so horribly unhappy in mine that my heart is nearly closed to hope." — "You are complaining," the old woman said to them; "alas! You haven't undergone misfortunes such as mine." Cunégonde almost started to laugh, and found that good woman quite comical to claim that she had been more unhappy than she herself. "Alas!" she told her, "my good woman, unless you have been raped by two Bulgarians, received two knife wounds in the belly, had two of your country houses demolished, had two mothers and two fathers butchered before your eyes, and seen two of your lovers whipped in an auto-da-fé, I don't see how you can surpass me; add to this that I was born a Baroness with seventy-two quarterings, and that I have been a cook." — "Mademoiselle," replied the old woman, "You don't know what my birth is; and if I showed you my behind, you would not have spoken as you did and you would suspend your judgment." This speech aroused extreme curiosity in the minds of Cunégonde and Candide. The old woman spoke to them as follows.

Chapitre Onzième

Histoire de la Vieille

"Je n'ai pas eu toujours les yeux éraillés et bordés d'écarlate; mon nez n'a pas toujours touché à mon menton, et je n'ai pas toujours été servante. Je suis la fille du pape Urbain X et de la princesse de Palestrine.* On m'éleva jusqu'à quatorze ans dans un palais auquel tous les châteaux de vos barons allemands n'auraient pas servi d'écurie; et une de mes robes valait mieux que toutes les magnificences de la Vestphalie. Je croissais en beauté, en grâces, en talents, au milieu des plaisirs, des respects, et des espérances: j'inspirais déjà de l'amour; ma gorge se formait; et quelle gorge! blanche, ferme, taillée comme celle de la Vénus de Médicis; et quels yeux! quelles paupières! quels sour-

* Voyez l'extrême discrétion de l'auteur! Il n'y eut jusqu'à présent aucun pape nommé Urbain X. Il craint de donner une bâtarde à un pape connu. Quelle circonspection! quelle délicatesse de conscience! [1]

[1] Voltaire's note, published posthumously. This is, of course, an ironic footnote. Voltaire had said far worse things about

Eleventh Chapter

The Old Woman's Story

"My eyes were not always bloodshot and red-rimmed; my nose did not always touch my chin, and I have not always been a servant. I am the daughter of Pope Urban X and the Princess of Palestrina.* Until I was fourteen I was brought up in a palace which all the country houses of your German Barons would not have served as stables; and one of my dresses was worth more than all the magnificences of Westphalia. I grew in beauty, grace, talent, in the midst of pleasures, respect, and hopes. I was already inspiring love, my breasts were forming; and what breasts! White, firm, sculptured like those of the Venus de Medici. And what eyes! What eyelids! What black eyebrows!

* Note the Author's extreme discretion! Until now there has been no pope called Urban X; he is afraid to give a bastard daughter to a known pope. What circumspection! What delicacy of conscience! [1]

popes in other works. The last pope called Urban was Urban VIII (1623–44).

cils noirs! quelles flammes brillaient dans mes deux prunelles, et effaçaient la scintillation des étoiles, comme me disaient les poètes du quartier. Les femmes qui m'habillaient et qui me déshabillaient tombaient en extase en me regardant par devant et par derrière; et tous les hommes auraient voulu être à leur place.

"Je fus fiancée à un prince souverain de Massa-Carrara. Quel prince! aussi beau que moi, pétri de douceur et d'agréments, brillant d'esprit et brûlant d'amour. Je l'aimais comme on aime pour la première fois, avec idolâtrie, avec emportement. Les noces furent préparées. C'était une pompe, une magnificence inouïe; c'étaient des fêtes, des carrousels, des opéra-buffa continuels; et toute l'Italie fit pour moi des sonnets dont il n'y eut pas un seul de passable. Je touchais au moment de mon bonheur, quand une vieille marquise qui avait été maîtresse de mon prince l'invita à prendre du chocolat chez elle: il mourut en moins de deux heures avec des convulsions épouvantables; mais ce n'est qu'une bagatelle. Ma mère, au désespoir, et bien moins affligée que moi, voulut s'arracher pour quelque temps à un séjour si funeste. Elle avait une très belle terre auprès de Gaiëte. Nous nous embarquâmes sur une galère du pays, dorée comme l'autel de Saint-Pierre de Rome. Voilà qu'un corsaire de Salé [2] fond sur nous et nous aborde; nos soldats se défendirent comme des

[2] A Moroccan port on the Atlantic ocean, which the Barbary pirates used as headquarters in the eighteenth century.

What flames glittered in my two irises and dimmed the glitter of the stars, as the poets of the neighborhood used to tell me. The women who dressed and undressed me fell into ecstasy when they looked at me in front and in the rear, and all the men would have liked to be in their place.

"I was engaged to a sovereign prince of Massa-Carrara. What a prince! As handsome as I, kneaded of sweetness and charm, sparkling with wit and ablaze with love. I loved him as one loves for the first time, with idolatry, with frenzy. The wedding feast was prepared. There was unheard-of pomp and magnificence; there were continual festivities, tilting matches, comic operas; and all of Italy wrote sonnets for me of which not a single one was tolerable. The moment of my happiness was near, when an old marquise who had been my prince's mistress invited him to have chocolate at her house. He died in less than two hours with frightful convulsions. But that's only a bagatelle. My mother, in despair, yet much less afflicted than I, tried to tear herself away for some time from such a painful habitation. She had a very handsome estate near Gaeta. We embarked on a local galley, gilded like the altar of St. Peter's of Rome. Here's where a corsair from Sallé [2] swoops on us and boards us; our soldiers defended themselves like soldiers of the Pope; they

81

soldats du pape: ils se mirent tous à genoux en jetant leurs armes, et en demandant au corsaire une absolution *in articulo mortis.*[3]

"Aussitôt on les dépouilla nus comme des singes, et ma mère aussi, nos filles d'honneur aussi, et moi aussi. C'est une chose admirable que la diligence avec laquelle ces messieurs déshabillent le monde. Mais ce qui me surprit davantage, c'est qu'ils nous mirent à tous le doigt dans un endroit où nous autres femmes nous ne nous laissons mettre d'ordinaire que des canules. Cette cérémonie me paraissait bien étrange: voilà comme on juge de tout quand on n'est pas sorti de son pays. J'appris bientôt que c'était pour voir si nous n'avions pas caché là quelques diamants: c'est un usage établi de temps immémorial parmi les nations policées qui courent sur mer. J'ai su que messieurs les religieux chevaliers de Malte n'y manquent jamais quand ils prennent des Turcs et des Turques; c'est une loi du droit des gens à laquelle on n'a jamais dérogé.

"Je ne vous dirai point combien il est dur pour une jeune princesse d'être menée esclave à Maroc avec sa mère. Vous concevez assez tout ce que nous eûmes à souffrir dans le vaisseau corsaire. Ma mère était encore très belle; nos filles d'honneur, nos simples femmes de chambre, avaient plus de charmes qu'on n'en peut trouver dans toute l'Afrique. Pour moi, j'étais ravissante, j'étais la beauté, la grâce même, et j'étais pucelle. Je ne le fus pas longtemps: cette fleur,

all fell on their knees and threw away their arms, and begged the pirates for absolution *in articulo mortis.*[3]

"They stripped them naked as monkeys immediately, and my mother too, our ladies of honor too, and me too. The diligence with which these gentlemen undress everybody is a wonderful thing. But what surprised me more is that they put their finger in a place in all of us where we women ordinarily allow nothing but the end of a syringe. That ceremony struck me as quite strange; that's how one judges everything when one has never left one's country. I soon learned that this was to see if we had hidden some diamonds there; it's a custom established from time immemorial among the civilized nations that sail the seas. I discovered that Messieurs the religious Knights of Malta never fail to do this when they capture Turkish men and women; it is a rule in international law that has never been questioned.

"I won't tell you how hard it is for a young princess to be carried to Morocco as a slave with her mother. You can imagine easily enough everything we had to suffer in the corsair's vessel. My mother was still very beautiful; our ladies of honor, our very chambermaids, had more charm than you could find in all of Africa. As for me, I was ravishing, I was beauty, grace itself, and I was a virgin. I was not so for long; that flower

[3] On the point of death.

qui avait été réservée pour le beau prince de Massa-Carrara, me fut ravie par le capitaine corsaire; c'était un nègre abominable, qui croyait encore me faire beaucoup d'honneur. Certes il fallait que Madame la princesse de Palestrine et moi fussions bien fortes pour résister à tout ce que nous éprouvâmes jusqu'à notre arrivée à Maroc! Mais passons; ce sont des choses si communes qu'elles ne valent pas la peine qu'on en parle.

"Maroc nageait dans le sang quand nous arrivâmes. Cinquante fils de l'empereur Mulei-Ismaël [4] avaient chacun leur parti: ce qui produisait en effet cinquante guerres civiles, de noirs contre noirs, de noirs contre basanés, de basanés contre basanés, de mulâtres contre mulâtres: c'était un carnage continuel dans toute l'étendue de l'empire.

"A peine fûmes-nous débarqués que des noirs d'une faction ennemie de celle de mon corsaire se présentèrent pour lui enlever son butin. Nous étions, après les diamants et l'or, ce qu'il avait de plus précieux. Je fus témoin d'un combat tel que vous n'en voyez jamais dans vos climats d'Europe. Les peuples septentrionaux n'ont pas le sang assez ardent; ils n'ont pas la rage des femmes au point où elle est commune en Afrique. Il semble que vos Européens aient du lait dans les veines; c'est du vitriol, c'est du feu, qui coule dans celles des habitants du mont Atlas et des pays voisins. On combattit avec la fureur des lions, des tigres

[4] Muley Ismael (1646–1727), Sultan of Morocco, was considered by Voltaire a bloodthirsty tyrant. After his death, his em-

which had been reserved for the handsome prince of Massa-Carrara was ravished from me by the corsair captain; he was a hideous Negro, who even thought he was doing me a great honor. Surely, Madame the Princess of Palestrina and I had to be very strong to endure everything we suffered until our arrival in Morocco. But, on with it; these are things so common that they are not worth talking about.

"Morocco was swimming in blood when we arrived. Fifty sons of the Emperor Muley Ismael [4] had each their party; which in fact produced fifty civil wars, of blacks against blacks, blacks against tans, tans against tans, mulattoes against mulattoes; in the whole extent of the empire there was continual carnage.

"We had hardly disembarked when a boat of one faction hostile to that of the corsair came up to carry off his booty. After the diamonds and the gold, we were the most precious thing he had. I was witness to a combat such as you never see in your European climes. The blood of northern peoples isn't ardent enough. They are not crazy for women to the point that is common in Africa. It seems that you Europeans have milk in your veins; it is vitriol, it is fire that courses in those of the inhabitants of Mount Atlas and neighboring countries. They battled with the fury of lions,

<hr />

pire was in fact afflicted by the civil war of two factions forming around two of his sons.

85

et des serpents de la contrée, pour savoir qui nous aurait. Un Maure saisit ma mère par le bras droit, le lieutenant de mon capitaine la retint par le bras gauche; un soldat maure la prit par une jambe, un de nos pirates la tenait par l'autre. Nos filles se trouvèrent presque toutes en un moment tirées ainsi à quatre soldats. Mon capitaine me tenait cachée derrière lui; il avait le cimeterre au poing, et tuait tout ce qui s'opposait à sa rage. Enfin, je vis toutes nos Italiennes et ma mère déchirées, coupées, massacrées par les monstres qui se les disputaient. Les captifs mes compagnons, ceux qui les avaient pris, soldats, matelots, noirs, basanés, blancs, mulâtres, et enfin mon capitaine, tout fut tué, et je demeurai mourante sur un tas de morts. Des scènes pareilles se passaient, comme on sait, dans l'étendue de plus de trois cents lieues,[5] sans qu'on manquât aux cinq prières par jour ordonnées par Mahomet.

"Je me débarrassai avec beaucoup de peine de la foule de tant de cadavres sanglants entassés, et je me traînai sous un grand oranger au bord d'un ruisseau voisin; j'y tombai d'effroi, de lassitude, d'horreur, de désespoir et de faim. Bientôt après, mes sens accablés se livrèrent à un sommeil qui tenait plus de l'évanouissement que du repos. J'étais dans cet état de faiblesse

[5] A league is three miles; it has been translated into miles throughout.

tigers, and serpents of the country, to see who would get us. One Moor seized my mother by the right arm, my captain's lieutenant held her back by the left arm; a Moorish soldier took her by one leg, one of our pirates held her by the other. In a moment nearly all of our ladies found themselves pulled in this manner by four soldiers. My captain kept me hidden behind him. He had a scimitar in his fist, and killed everyone who opposed his fury. Finally I saw all our Italian women and my mother torn apart, cut up, massacred by the monsters who were fighting over them. The captain, my companions, those who had taken them, soldiers, sailors, blacks, tans, whites, mulattoes, and at last my captain, all were killed, and I remained dying on a pile of dead. As you know, similar scenes were going on in an area of more than nine hundred miles,[5] without anyone omitting the five prayers a day ordained by Mahomet.

"With great difficulty I extricated myself from the crowd of so many bloody, piled-up corpses, and dragged myself under a great orange tree at the edge of the neighboring stream; there I dropped down from fright, lassitude, horror, despair, and hunger. Soon afterwards, my overwhelmed senses gave themselves up to the sleep which was closer to fainting than to repose. I was in

et d'insensibilité, entre la mort et la vie, quand je me sentis pressée de quelque chose qui s'agitait sur mon corps; j'ouvris les yeux, je vis un homme blanc et de bonne mine qui soupirait, et qui disait entre ses dents: *O che sciagura d'essere senza coglioni!*

this state of weakness and insensibility between life and death, when I felt myself pressed down by something that was moving on my body; I opened my eyes, I saw a white man of good appearance who muttered between his teeth: *O what misery to be without balls!*

Chapitre Douzième

Suite des Malheurs de la Vieille

"Etonnée et ravie d'entendre la langue de ma patrie, et non moins surprise des paroles que proférait cet homme, je lui répondis qu'il y avait de plus grands malheurs que celui dont il se plaignait. Je l'instruisis en peu de mots des horreurs que j'avais essuyées, et je retombai en faiblesse. Il m'emporta dans une maison voisine, me fit mettre au lit, me fit donner à manger, me servit, me consola, me flatta, me dit qu'il n'avait rien vu de si beau que moi, et que jamais il n'avait tant regretté ce que personne ne pouvait lui rendre. 'Je suis né à Naples, me dit-il; on y chaponne deux ou trois mille enfants tous les ans; les uns en meurent, les autres acquièrent une voix plus belle que celle des femmes,[1] les autres vont gouverner des États. On me fit cette opération avec un très grand succès, et j'ai été musicien de la chapelle de Madame la princesse de Palestrine. — De ma mère, m'écriai-je. — De

[1] This is an allusion to Carlo Broschi, known as Farinelli (1705–82), a celebrated singer who acquired considerable influ-

Twelfth Chapter

Continuation of the Old Woman's Misfortunes

"Amazed and delighted to hear the language of my country, and no less surprised at the words this man was uttering, I replied that there were greater miseries than the ones of which he complained. I informed him in a few words of the horrors I had suffered, and I fell back into a faint. He brought me to a neighboring house, had me put to bed, had food given me, served me, consoled me, flattered me, told me that he had never seen anything so beautiful as me, and that he had never regretted so much what no one could give back to him. 'I was born in Naples,' he told me; 'there they caponize two or three thousand children every year; some die of it, others acquire a voice more beautiful than that of women,[1] still others go and govern states. They performed this operation on me with very great success, and I was a musician in the chapel of Madame the Princess of Palestrina.' — 'Of my mother!'

ence at the courts of two Spanish kings, Philip v and Ferdinand vi.

votre mère! s'écria-t-il en pleurant; quoi! vous seriez cette jeune princesse que j'ai élevée jusqu'à l'âge de six ans, et qui promettait déjà d'être aussi belle que vous êtes? — C'est moi-même; ma mère est à quatre cents pas d'ici, coupée en quartiers sous un tas de morts . . .'

"Je lui contai tout ce qui m'était arrivé; il me conta aussi ses aventures, et m'apprit comment il avait été envoyé chez le roi de Maroc par une puissance chrétienne, pour conclure avec ce monarque un traité par lequel on lui fournirait de la poudre, des canons, et des vaisseaux, pour l'aider à exterminer le commerce des autres chrétiens.[2] 'Ma mission est faite, dit cet honnête eunuque; je vais m'embarquer à Ceuta, et je vous ramènerai en Italie. *Ma che sciagura d'essere senza coglioni!*'

"Je le remerciai avec des larmes d'attendrissement; et au lieu de me mener en Italie, il me conduisit à Alger, et me vendit au dey de cette province. A peine fus-je vendue que cette peste qui a fait le tour de l'Afrique, de l'Asie et de l'Europe, se déclara dans Alger avec fureur. Vous avez vu des tremblements de terre; mais, Mademoiselle, avez-vous jamais eu la peste? — Jamais, répondit la baronne.

"Si vous l'aviez eue, reprit la vieille, vous avoueriez qu'elle est bien au-dessus d'un tremblement de terre. Elle est fort commune en Afrique; j'en fus attaquée.

[2] During the War of the Spanish Succession (1701–13), Muley Ismael's aid was solicited by several European nations. See Voltaire's *Siècle de Louis XIV*: "The king of Portugal, the prince of Darmstadt, etc., even implored the help of the king of

I exclaimed. — 'Of your mother!' he exclaimed, weeping. 'What! Are you then that young princess whom I brought up to the age of six, and who already promised to be as beautiful as you are?' — 'That is me; my mother is four hundred feet from here, cut into quarters under a pile of dead . . .'

"I told him everything that had happened to me; he told me his adventures too, and informed me how he had been sent to the King of Morocco by a Christian power, to conclude a treaty with that monarch by which he would be furnished with gunpowder, cannons, and vessels to help him exterminate the commerce of other Christians.[2] 'My mission is completed,' said this honest eunuch; 'I am going to embark at Ceuta, and I'll take you back to Italy, *but what a misery to be without balls!'*

"I thanked him with tears of tenderness; and instead of taking me to Italy, he brought me to Algiers, and sold me to the Dey of that province. Hardly had I been sold when that pest which has spread all over Africa, Asia, and Europe, broke out in Algiers with fury. You have seen earthquakes; but, Mademoiselle, have you ever had the plague?" — "Never," replied the Baroness.

"If you had had it," the old woman continued, "you would concede that it is far worse than an earthquake. It is very common in Africa; I was attacked by it. Imag-

Morocco. Not merely did they make treaties with this barbarian, to get horses and grain, but they asked for troops." *Oeuvres*, XIV, 354.

Figurez-vous quelle situation pour la fille d'un pape, âgée de quinze ans, qui en trois mois de temps avait éprouvé la pauvreté, l'esclavage, avait été violée presque tous les jours, avait vu couper sa mère en quatre, avait essuyé la faim et la guerre, et mourait pestiférée dans Alger. Je n'en mourus pourtant pas; mais mon eunuque et le dey, et presque tout le sérail d'Alger périrent.

"Quand les premiers ravages de cette épouvantable peste furent passés, on vendit les esclaves du dey. Un marchand m'acheta et me mena à Tunis; il me vendit à un autre marchand, qui me revendit à Tripoli; de Tripoli je fus revendue à Alexandrie, d'Alexandrie revendue à Smyrne, de Smyrne à Constantinople. J'appartins enfin à un aga des janissaires,[3] qui fut bientôt commandé pour aller défendre Azof contre les Russes qui l'assiégeaient.[4]

"L'aga, qui était un très galant homme, mena avec lui tout son sérail, et nous logea dans un petit fort sur les Palus-Méotides,[5] gardé par deux eunuques noirs et vingt soldats. On tua prodigieusement de Russes, mais ils nous le rendirent bien. Azof fut mis à feu et à sang, et on ne pardonna ni au sexe ni à l'âge; il ne resta que notre petit fort; les ennemis voulurent nous prendre par la famine. Les vingt janissaires avaient juré de ne se jamais rendre. Les extrémités de la faim où ils furent réduits les contraignirent à manger nos deux eunuques, de peur de violer leur serment. Au

[3] A chief of the footguard of the Turkish sultans.

[4] Azov, then a part of the Turkish Empire, was besieged by

ine what a situation for a Pope's daughter, aged fifteen, who in three months' time had undergone poverty, slavery, had been raped almost every day, had seen her mother cut in four, had endured hunger and war, and was dying plague-stricken in Algiers. Yet, I did not die of it; but my eunuch and the Dey, and almost all the seraglio of Algiers perished.

"When the first ravages of this dreadful plague were over, the slaves of the Dey were sold. A merchant bought me and brought me to Tunis; he sold me to another merchant who resold me at Tripoli; from Tripoli I was resold to Alexandria, from Alexandria resold to Smyrna, from Smyrna to Constantinople. Finally I belonged to an Aga of the Janizaries,[3] who was soon ordered to go and defend Azov against the Russians who were besieging it.[4]

"The Aga, who was a man of great gallantry, brought his whole seraglio with him, and housed us in a little fort on the Maeotian Marsh,[5] guarded by two black eunuchs and twenty soldiers. Russians were killed in prodigious numbers, but they gave as good as they got. Azov was put to fire and sword, and no mercy was given either to sex or to age; nothing remained but our little fort; the enemy tried to take us by starvation. The twenty Janizaries had sworn never to surrender. The extremities of hunger to which they were reduced constrained them to eat our two eunuchs, for fear of

the Russians several times.

[5] Old name for the Sea of Azov, north of the Black Sea.

bout de quelques jours, ils résolurent de manger les femmes.

"Nous avions un iman [6] très pieux et très compatissant, qui leur fit un beau sermon par lequel il leur persuada de ne nous pas tuer tout à fait. 'Coupez, dit-il, seulement une fesse à chacune de ces dames, vous ferez très bonne chère; s'il faut y revenir, vous en aurez encore autant dans quelques jours; le ciel vous saura gré d'une action si charitable, et vous serez secourus.'

"Il avait beaucoup d'éloquence; il les persuada. On nous fit cette horrible opération. L'iman nous appliqua le même baume qu'on met aux enfants qu'on vient de circoncire. Nous étions toutes à la mort.

"A peine les janissaires eurent-ils fait le repas que nous leur avions fourni que les Russes arrivent sur des bateaux plats; il ne réchappa pas un janissaire. Les Russes ne firent aucune attention à l'état où nous étions. Il y a partout des chirurgiens français: un d'eux, qui était fort adroit, prit soin de nous; il nous guérit, et je me souviendrai toute ma vie que, quand mes plaies furent bien fermées, il me fit des propositions. Au reste, il nous dit à toutes de nous consoler; il nous assura que dans plusieurs sièges pareille chose était arrivée, et que c'était la loi de la guerre.

"Dès que mes compagnes purent marcher, on les fit aller à Moscou. J'échus en partage à un boïard qui

[6] A Moslem priest.

violating their oath. After a few days they resolved to eat the women.

"We had among us a very pious and very compassionate Imam,[6] who gave them a fine sermon by which he persuaded them not to kill us completely. 'Merely cut off one buttock from each of these ladies,' he said, 'you'll live very well; if you have to come back to that, you'll still have as much in a few days; heaven will be grateful to you for such a charitable action, and you will be rescued.'

"He had great eloquence; he persuaded them. They performed this horrible operation. The Imam applied to us the same balm which they put on children who have just been circumcised. We were all at the point of death.

"Hardly had the Janizaries completed the meal we had furnished them, when the Russians arrived in flat-bottomed boats; not one Janizary escaped. The Russians paid no attention whatever to the condition we were in. There are French surgeons everywhere; one of them, who was extremely skillful, took care of us; he cured us, and I'll remember all my life that when my wounds were quite closed, he propositioned me. In addition, he told us all to console ourselves; he assured us that similar things had happened in numerous sieges and that this was the law of war.

"As soon as my companions could walk, they were sent to Moscow. I fell to the lot of a Boyar who made

me fit sa jardinière, et qui me donnait vingt coups de fouet par jour. Mais ce seigneur ayant été roué au bout de deux ans avec une trentaine de boïards pour quelque tracasserie de cour, je profitai de cette aventure; je m'enfuis; je traversai toute la Russie; je fus longtemps servante de cabaret à Riga, puis à Rostock, à Vismar, à Leipsick, à Cassel, à Utrecht, à Leyde, à la Haye, à Rotterdam; j'ai vieilli dans la misère et dans l'opprobre, n'ayant que la moitié d'un derrière, me souvenant toujours que j'étais fille d'un pape; je voulus cent fois me tuer, mais j'aimais encore la vie. Cette faiblesse ridicule est peut-être un de nos penchants les plus funestes: car y a-t-il rien de plus sot que de vouloir porter continuellement un fardeau qu'on veut toujours jeter par terre; d'avoir son être en horreur, et de tenir à son être? Enfin de caresser le serpent qui nous dévore, jusqu'à ce qu'il nous ait mangé le cœur?

"J'ai vu dans les pays que le sort m'a fait parcourir, et dans les cabarets où j'ai servi, un nombre prodigieux de personnes qui avaient leur existence en exécration; mais je n'en ai vu que douze qui aient mis volontairement fin à leur misère: trois nègres, quatre Anglais, quatre Genevois et un professeur allemand nommé Robeck.[7] J'ai fini par être servante chez le juif don Issachar; il me mit auprès de vous, ma belle demoiselle; je me suis attachée à votre destinée, et j'ai été plus

[7] Johann Robeck (1672–1735), born in Sweden, went to Germany and became a Jesuit, but left the order a year before his death. He probably committed suicide; his book on the subject was published posthumously. Not being a Christian, Voltaire

me his gardener and who gave me twenty lashes a day; but after two years this lord was broken on the wheel with some thirty other Boyars for some mischief at court, and I took advantage of this adventure; I fled; I crossed the whole of Russia; for a long time I was a servant at an inn at Riga, then at Rostock, at Wismar, at Leipzig, Cassel, Utrecht, Leyden, the Hague, Rotterdam; I have grown old in misery and opprobrium, having only half of a behind, always remembering that I was the daughter of a Pope; I wanted to kill myself a hundred times, but I still loved life. This ridiculous weakness is perhaps one of our most baleful inclinations; for is there anything more foolish than to want to bear continually a burden that one steadily wants to throw to the ground? To hold one's being in horror, and to cling to one's being? In a word, to caress the snake that devours us until it has eaten our heart?

"In the countries which fate has made me travel through, and in the inns in which I have served, I have seen a prodigious number of persons who hated their existence; but I have seen only twelve who voluntarily put an end to their misery; three Negroes, four Englishmen, four Genevans, and a German professor called Robeck.[7] I ended by being a servant to the Jew Don Issachar; he put me in your service, my beautiful lady; I have attached myself to your destiny, and I have

had no doctrinal objections to suicide, and discussed the question several times. In his *Lettres philosophiques* (1734), his affectionate report on England, he noted that Englishmen were peculiarly given to suicide.

occupée de vos aventures que des miennes. Je ne vous aurais même jamais parlé de mes malheurs, si vous ne m'aviez pas un peu piquée, et s'il n'était d'usage dans un vaisseau de conter des histoires pour se désennuyer. Enfin, Mademoiselle, j'ai de l'expérience, je connais le monde; donnez-vous un plaisir, engagez chaque passager à vous conter son histoire, et s'il s'en trouve un seul qui n'ait souvent maudit sa vie, qui ne se soit souvent dit à lui-même qu'il était le plus malheureux des hommes, jetez-moi dans la mer la tête la première."

been more concerned with your adventures than with mine. I should never even have mentioned my miseries to you if you had not goaded me a little, and if it were not the custom to tell stories on shipboard to escape boredom. In a word, Mademoiselle, I have experience, I know the world; amuse yourself, get each passenger to tell you his story, and if there is a single one among them who has not often cursed his life, who has not often said to himself that he is the most miserable of men, throw me into the sea head first."

Chapitre Treizième

*Comment Candide Fut Obligé de Se Séparer de
la Belle Cunégonde et de la Vieille*

La belle Cunégonde, ayant entendu l'histoire de la
vieille, lui fit toutes les politesses qu'on devait à une
personne de son rang et de son mérite. Elle accepta
la proposition; elle engagea tous les passagers l'un
après l'autre à lui conter leurs aventures. Candide et
elle avouèrent que la vieille avait raison. "C'est bien
dommage, disait Candide, que le sage Pangloss ait été
pendu contre la coutume dans un auto-da-fé; il nous
dirait des choses admirables sur le mal physique et sur
le mal moral qui couvrent la terre et la mer, et je me
sentirais assez de force pour oser lui faire respectueu-
sement quelques objections."

A mesure que chacun racontait son histoire, le vais-
seau avançait. On aborda dans Buenos-Ayres. Cuné-
gonde, le capitaine Candide et la vieille allèrent chez
le gouverneur Don Fernando d'Ibaraa, y Figueora, y
Mascarenes, y Lampourdos, y Souza. Ce seigneur avait
une fierté convenable à un homme qui portait tant de
noms. Il parlait aux hommes avec le dédain le plus

Thirteenth Chapter

How Candide Was Forced to Part from the Lovely Cunégonde and the Old Woman

Lovely Cunégonde, having heard the old woman's story, showed her all the courtesy owed to a person of her rank and merit. She accepted the proposal; she got all the passengers, one after the other, to tell their adventures. Candide and she admitted that the old woman was right. "It's a great pity," said Candide, "that the wise Pangloss should have been hanged contrary to custom in an auto-da-fé; he would tell us wonderful things about the physical evil and the moral evil that cover land and sea, and I would feel enough strength in me to dare, respectfully, to make some objections."

While each was narrating his story, the vessel moved forward. They landed in Buenos Aires. Cunégonde, Captain Candide, and the old woman went to see the governor, Don Fernando d'Ibaraa, y Figueora, y Mascarenes, y Lampourdos, y Souza. This lord had a pride appropriate to a man who bore so many names. He spoke to men with the noblest disdain, carrying his

noble, portant le nez si haut, élevant si impitoyablement la voix, prenant un ton si imposant, affectant une démarche si altière, que tous ceux qui le saluaient étaient tentés de le battre. Il aimait les femmes à la fureur. Cunégonde lui parut ce qu'il avait jamais vu de plus beau. La première chose qu'il fit fut de demander si elle n'était point la femme du capitaine. L'air dont il fit cette question alarma Candide: il n'osa pas dire qu'elle était sa femme, parce qu'en effet elle ne l'était point; il n'osait pas dire que c'était sa sœur, parce qu'elle ne l'était pas non plus; et quoique ce mensonge officieux eût été autrefois très à la mode chez les anciens,[1] et qu'il pût être utile aux modernes, son âme était trop pure pour trahir la vérité. "Mademoiselle Cunégonde, dit-il, doit me faire l'honneur de m'épouser, et nous supplions Votre Excellence de daigner faire notre noce."

Don Fernando d'Ibaraa, y Figueora, y Mascarenes, y Lampourdos, y Souza, relevant sa moustache, sourit amèrement, et ordonna au capitaine Candide d'aller faire la revue de sa compagnie. Candide obéit; le gouverneur demeura avec Mademoiselle Cunégonde. Il lui déclara sa passion, lui protesta que le lendemain il l'épouserait à la face de l'Église, ou autrement, ainsi qu'il plairait à ses charmes. Cunégonde lui demanda un quart d'heure pour se recueillir, pour consulter la vieille, et pour se déterminer.

[1] A pointed allusion to Abraham and Sarah (Genesis 12:12–13). Voltaire, in his later years, never tired of trying to discredit

nose so high, raising his voice so pitilessly, taking so impressive a tone, affecting so lofty a bearing, that all those who addressed him were tempted to hit him. He loved women to frenzy. Cunégonde seemed to him the most beautiful one he had ever seen. The first thing he did was to ask if she were not the Captain's wife. The manner in which he asked that question alarmed Candide; he dared not say that she was his wife because in fact she was not; he dared not say that she was his sister, because she was not that either; and even though this official lie had once been very fashionable among the ancients,[1] and could be useful to the moderns, his soul was too pure to be false to truth. "Mademoiselle Cunégonde," he said, "will do me the honor of marrying me, and we beg Your Excellency to perform our wedding ceremony."

Don Fernando d'Ibaraa, y Figueora, y Mascarenes, y Lampourdos, y Souza, twirling his moustache, smiled bitterly and ordered Captain Candide to go pass his company in review. Candide obeyed; the governor remained with Mademoiselle Cunégonde. He declared his passion to her, protested to her that the next day he would marry her with the Church's blessing or otherwise, just as it might please her charms. Cunégonde asked him for a quarter of an hour to collect herself, to consult the old woman, and to decide.

the Jews of the Bible. On Abraham's "official lie" see Voltaire's article on "*Abraham*" in the *Dictionnaire philosophique*.

La vieille dit à Cunégonde: "Mademoiselle, vous avez soixante et douze quartiers, et pas une obole; il ne tient qu'à vous d'être la femme du plus grand seigneur de l'Amérique méridionale, qui a une très belle moustache; est-ce à vous de vous piquer d'une fidélité à toute épreuve? Vous avez été violée par les Bulgares; un juif et un inquisiteur ont eu vos bonnes grâces: les malheurs donnent des droits. J'avoue que, si j'étais à votre place, je ne ferais aucun scrupule d'épouser monsieur le gouverneur et de faire la fortune de Monsieur le capitaine Candide." Tandis que la vieille parlait avec toute la prudence que l'âge et l'expérience donnent, on vit entrer dans le port un petit vaisseau; il portait un alcade et des alguazils,[2] et voici ce qui était arrivé.

La vieille avait très bien deviné que ce fut un cordelier à la grande manche qui vola l'argent et les bijoux de Cunégonde dans la ville de Badajos, lorsqu'elle fuyait en hâte avec Candide. Ce moine voulut vendre quelques-unes des pierreries à un joaillier. Le marchand les reconnut pour celles du grand inquisiteur. Le cordelier, avant d'être pendu, avoua qu'il les avait volées: il indiqua les personnes et la route qu'elles prenaient. La fuite de Cunégonde et de Candide était déjà connue. On les suivit à Cadix; on envoya, sans perdre de temps, un vaisseau à leur poursuite. Le vaisseau était déjà dans le port de Buenos-Ayres. Le bruit se répandit

[2] These are, respectively, the Spanish names given to certain municipal magistrates, and to certain police officers.

The old woman said to Cunégonde: "Mademoiselle Cunégonde, you have seventy-two quarterings and not an obole; it's entirely up to you to be the wife of the greatest lord in South America, who has a very handsome moustache; are you the one to be a stickler for an unshakable fidelity? You have been raped by the Bulgarians; the Jew and the Inquisitor have enjoyed your favors; misfortunes confer rights. I confess that if I were in your place I would have no scruple over marrying Monsieur the Governor and making a fortune for Monsieur the Captain Candide." While the old woman was speaking with all the prudence that age and experience give, a little vessel was seen entering the port; it carried an Alcaide and some Alguazils,[2] and here's what happened.

The old woman had guessed very well that it was a long-sleeved Franciscan who stole Cunégonde's money and jewels in the town of Badajoz when she was fleeing in haste with Candide. This monk tried to sell several of the precious stones to a jeweler. The merchant recognized them as those of the Grand Inquisitor. The Franciscan, before being hanged, confessed that he had stolen them, he indicated the persons and the route they were taking. The flight of Cunégonde and Candide was already known. They followed them to Cadiz; without losing time they sent a vessel in pursuit of them. The vessel was already in the harbor of Buenos Aires. The rumor spread that an Alcaide was

qu'un alcade allait débarquer, et qu'on poursuivait les meurtriers de monseigneur le grand inquisiteur. La prudente vieille vit dans l'instant tout ce qui était à faire. "Vous ne pouvez fuir, dit-elle à Cunégonde, et vous n'avez rien à craindre; ce n'est pas vous qui avez tué monseigneur, et d'ailleurs le gouverneur, qui vous aime, ne souffrira pas qu'on vous maltraite; demeurez." Elle court sur-le-champ à Candide: "Fuyez, dit-elle, ou dans une heure vous allez être brûlé." Il n'y avait pas un moment à perdre; mais comment se séparer de Cunégonde, et où se réfugier?

about to disembark, and that the murderers of Monseigneur the Grand Inquisitor were being pursued. The prudent old woman saw in a moment all that had to be done. "You cannot flee," she said to Cunégonde, "and you have nothing to fear; it wasn't you who killed Monseigneur, and besides the governor, who loves you, will not permit them to mistreat you; stay." Right away she runs to Candide: "Flee," she says, "or you'll be burned within an hour." There was not a moment to lose, but how to part from Cunégonde, and where to take refuge?

Chapitre Quatorzième

Comment Candide et Cacambo Furent Reçus Chez les Jésuites du Paraguai

Candide avait amené de Cadix un valet tel qu'on en trouve beaucoup sur les côtes d'Espagne et dans les colonies. C'était un quart d'Espagnol, né d'un métis dans le Tucuman;[1] il avait été enfant de chœur, sacristain, matelot, moine, facteur, soldat, laquais. Il s'appelait Cacambo, et aimait fort son maître, parce que son maître était un fort bon homme. Il sella au plus vite les deux chevaux andalous. "Allons, mon maître, suivons le conseil de la vieille; partons, et courons sans regarder derrière nous." Candide versa des larmes. "O ma chère Cunégonde! faut-il vous abandonner dans le temps que monsieur le gouverneur va faire nos noces! Cunégonde amenée de si loin, que deviendrez-vous? — Elle deviendra ce qu'elle pourra, dit Cacambo; les femmes ne sont jamais embarrassées d'elles; Dieu y pourvoit; courons. — Où me mènes-tu? où allons-nous? que ferons-nous sans Cunégonde? disait Candide. — Par St. Jacques de Compostelle, dit Ca-

[1] Province of Argentina, north-west of Buenos Aires.

Fourteenth Chapter

How Candide and Cacambo Were Received by the Jesuits of Paraguay

Candide had brought from Cadiz a valet such as one often finds on the coast of Spain and in the colonies. He was one-quarter Spanish, born of a mestizo in Tucuman; [1] he had been a choirboy, a sacristan, sailor, monk, salesman, soldier, lackey. His name was Cacambo, and he loved his master greatly, because his master was a very good man. He saddled the two Andalusian horses as fast as possible. "Let's go, my master, let's follow the old woman's advice; let's leave and run without looking behind us." Candide shed tears: "Oh my dear Cunégonde! Must you be abandoned just when Monsieur the Governor is about to perform our marriage! Cunégonde, brought from so far, what will become of you?" — "Let become of her what may," said Cacambo; "women are never at a loss about what to do; God takes care of them; let's run." — "Where are you taking me? Where are we going? What shall we do without Cunégonde?" said Candide. — "By St. James of Compostella," said Cacambo, "you

cambo, vous alliez faire la guerre aux jésuites; allons la faire pour eux: je sais assez les chemins, je vous mènerai dans leur royaume, ils seront charmés d'avoir un capitaine qui fasse l'exercice à la bulgare; vous ferez une fortune prodigieuse; quand on n'a pas son compte dans un monde, on le trouve dans un autre. C'est un très grand plaisir de voir et de faire des choses nouvelles."

"Tu as donc été déjà dans le Paraguai? dit Candide. —Eh vraiment oui! dit Cacambo; j'ai été cuistre dans le collège de l'Assomption, et je connais le gouvernement de Los Padres [2] comme je connais les rues de Cadix. C'est une chose admirable que ce gouvernement. Le royaume a déjà plus de trois cents lieues de diamètre; il est divisé en trente provinces. Los Padres y ont tout, et les peuples rien; c'est le chef-d'œuvre de la raison et de la justice. Pour moi, je ne vois rien de si divin que Los Padres, qui font ici la guerre au roi d'Espagne et au roi de Portugal, et qui en Europe confessent ces rois; qui tuent ici des Espagnols, et qui à Madrid les envoient au ciel: cela me ravit; avançons: vous allez être le plus heureux de tous les hommes. Quel plaisir auront Los Padres quand ils sauront qu'il leur vient un capitaine qui sait l'exercice bulgare!"

Dès qu'ils furent arrivés à la première barrière, Cacambo dit à la garde avancée qu'un capitaine deman-

[2] "The Fathers," a less than affectionate name for the Jesuits. Voltaire, who had been educated in a Jesuit school and retained his respect for some Jesuit scholars to the end of his life, mercilessly lampooned the order whenever he could. In 1758, prob-

were going to make war on the Jesuits; let's make it for them; I know the roads well enough, I'll lead you to their kingdom, they will be delighted to have a captain who drills in Bulgarian style; you will make a prodigious fortune; when you don't get justice in one world, you find it in another. It's a very great pleasure to see and do new things."

"Then you have already been in Paraguay?" said Candide. — "Oh indeed, yes!" said Cacambo. "I was a servant in the School of the Assumption, and I know the government of Los Padres [2] as I know the streets of Cadiz. It's a wonderful thing, this government. The kingdom already has more than nine hundred miles in diameter; it is divided into thirty provinces. Los Padres have everything there and the people nothing; it is the masterpiece of reason and justice. As for myself, I know nothing so divine as Los Padres, who make war on the King of Spain and the King of Portugal here, and who in Europe are confessors to these kings; who kills Spaniards here, and send them to heaven in Madrid; that delights me; let's go forward; you are going to be the happiest of all men. What pleasure Los Padres will have when they learn that a captain is coming to them who knows the Bulgarian drill!"

As soon as they had arrived at the first barrier, Cacambo told the outpost that the captain asked to speak

ably while he was working on *Candide*, he wrote a chapter for his *Essai sur les moeurs* dealing with the so-called Jesuit "kingdom" in Paraguay (see *Oeuvres*, xii, 424–8). The word "kingdom" is a gross exaggeration for "strong influence."

dait à parler à monseigneur le commandant. On alla avertir la grande garde. Un officier paraguain courut aux pieds du commandant lui donner part de la nouvelle. Candide et Cacambo furent d'abord désarmés; on se saisit de leurs deux chevaux andalous. Les deux étrangers sont introduits au milieu de deux files de soldats; le commandant était au bout, le bonnet à trois cornes en tête, la robe retroussée, l'épée au côté, l'esponton à la main. Il fit un signe; aussitôt vingt-quatre soldats entourent les deux nouveaux venus. Un sergent leur dit qu'il faut attendre, que le commandant ne peut leur parler, que le révérend père provincial ne permet pas qu'aucun Espagnol ouvre la bouche qu'en sa présence, et demeure plus de trois heures dans le pays. "Et où est le révérend père provincial? dit Cacambo. — Il est à la parade après avoir dit sa messe, répondit le sergent, et vous ne pourrez baiser ses éperons que dans trois heures. — Mais, dit Cacambo, monsieur le capitaine, qui meurt de faim comme moi, n'est point Espagnol, il est Allemand; ne pourrions-nous point déjeuner en attendant Sa Révérence?"

Le sergent alla sur-le-champ rendre compte de ce discours au commandant. "Dieu soit béni! dit ce seigneur; puisqu'il est Allemand, je peux lui parler; qu'on le mène dans ma feuillée." Aussitôt on conduit Candide dans un cabinet de verdure orné d'une très jolie colonnade de marbre vert et or, et de treillages qui renfermaient des perroquets, des colibris,[3] des oiseaux-mouches, des pintades, et tous les oiseaux les plus rares.

[3] A Caribbean word, referring to a kind of hummingbird.

to Monseigneur the Commander. They went to notify the chief guard. A Paraguayan officer ran to the feet of the Commander to give him the news. First Candide and Cacambo were disarmed; their two Andalusian horses were seized. The two foreigners are brought in the midst of two ranks of soldiers; the Commander was at the end, his three-cornered hat on his head, his gown tucked up, his sword at his side, his half-pike in his hand. He makes a sign; immediately twenty-four soldiers surround the two newcomers. A sergeant tells them that they must wait, that the Commander cannot speak to them, that the Reverend Provincial Father does not permit any Spaniard to open his mouth except in his presence, and remain any more than three hours in the country. "And where is the Reverend Provincial Father?" said Cacambo. — "He is at the parade after having said his Mass," replied the sergeant, "and you won't be able to kiss his spurs until three hours from now." — "But," said Cacambo, "Monsieur the Captain, who is dying of hunger like me, is not a Spaniard, he is a German; couldn't we have lunch while waiting for His Reverence?"

Right away the sergeant went to report these words to the Commander. "God be praised!" said this lord, "if he is German I can talk to him; let him be brought to my arbor." Candide is immediately taken into a leafy summer house, decorated with a pretty colonnade of green and gold marble, and with trellises which held parakeets, colibris,³ hummingbirds, guinea hens, and all

Un excellent déjeuner était préparé dans des vases d'or; et tandis que les Paraguains mangèrent du maïs dans des écuelles de bois, en plein champ, à l'ardeur du soleil, le révérend père commandant entra dans la feuillée.

C'était un très beau jeune homme, le visage plein, assez blanc, haut en couleur, le sourcil relevé, l'œil vif, l'oreille rouge, les lèvres vermeilles, l'air fier, mais d'un fierté qui n'était ni celle d'un Espagnol ni celle d'un jésuite. On rendit à Candide et à Cacambo leurs armes, qu'on leur avait saisies, ainsi que les deux chevaux andalous; Cacambo leur fit manger l'avoine auprès de la feuillée, ayant toujours l'œil sur eux, crainte de surprise.

Candide baisa d'abord le bas de la robe du commandant, ensuite ils se mirent à table. "Vous êtes donc Allemand? lui dit le jésuite en cette langue. — Oui, mon révérend père," dit Candide. L'un et l'autre, en prononçant ces paroles, se regardaient avec une extrême surprise et une émotion dont ils n'étaient pas les maîtres. "Et de quel pays d'Allemagne êtes-vous? dit le jésuite. — De la sale province de Vestphalie, dit Candide: je suis né dans le château de Thunder-ten-tronckh. — O Ciel! est-il possible! s'écria le commandant. — Quel miracle! s'écria Candide. — Serait-ce vous! dit le commandant. — Cela n'est pas possible," dit Candide. Ils se laissent tomber tous deux à la renverse, ils s'embrassent, ils versent des ruisseaux de larmes.[4] "Quoi!

[4] See Chapter 7, note 2: Voltaire's parody of sentimental recognition scenes is even more devastating here, since it describes the effusions of two men.

the rarest of birds. An excellent lunch stood prepared in golden vessels; and while the Paraguayans ate corn from wooden bowls, in the open fields, in the blazing sun, the Reverend Father Commander entered the arbor.

He was a very handsome young man, round faced, quite white skinned, red-cheeked, with arched eyebrows, lively eyes, red ears, vermilion lips, a proud air, but with a pride that was neither that of a Spaniard nor that of a Jesuit. Candide and Cacambo had their arms returned to them, which had been taken from them, as well as the two Andalusian horses; Cacambo fed them oats near the arbor, constantly keeping his eye on them, for fear of surprise.

Candide first kissed the hem of the Commander's robe, then they sat down to dinner. "So, you're German?" the Jesuit said to him in that language. — "Yes, my Reverend Father," said Candide. Each of them, pronouncing these words, looked at the other with extreme surprise and an emotion they could not master. "And what German state are you from?" said the Jesuit. — "From the filthy province of Westphalia," said Candide; "I was born in the country house of Thunder-ten-tronckh." — "Oh Heavens! Is it possible!" exclaimed the Commander. — "What a miracle!" exclaimed Candide. — "Could it be you?" said the Commander. — "It's not possible," said Candide. They both dropped back, they embraced, they shed streams of tears.[4] "What! Can it be you, my Reverend Father?

serait-ce vous, mon révérend père? vous, le frère de la belle Cunégonde! vous, qui fûtes tué par les Bulgares! vous, le fils de monsieur le baron! vous, jésuite au Paraguai! Il faut avouer que ce monde est une étrange chose. O Pangloss! Pangloss! que vous seriez aise si vous n'aviez pas été pendu!"

Le commandant fit retirer les esclaves nègres et les Paraguains qui servaient à boire dans des gobelets de cristal de roche. Il remercia Dieu et St. Ignace [5] mille fois; il serrait Candide entre ses bras; leurs visages étaient baignés de pleurs. "Vous seriez bien plus étonné, plus attendri, plus hors de vous-même, dit Candide, si je vous disais que Mademoiselle Cunégonde, votre sœur, que vous avez cru éventrée, est pleine de santé. — Où? — Dans votre voisinage, chez monsieur le gouverneur de Buenos-Ayres; et je venais pour vous faire la guerre." Chaque mot qu'ils prononcèrent dans cette longue conversation accumulait prodige sur prodige. Leur âme tout entière volait sur leur langue, était attentive dans leurs oreilles, et étincelante dans leurs yeux. Comme ils étaient Allemands, ils tinrent table longtemps en attendant le révérend père provincial; et le commandant parla ainsi á son cher Candide.

[5] Ignatius de Loyola (1491–1556), the Spaniard who founded the Jesuit order.

You, the beautiful Cunégonde's brother! You, who were killed by the Bulgarians! You, the son of Monsieur the Baron! You, Jesuit of Paraguay! It must be confessed that this world is a strange thing. Oh Pangloss! Pangloss! How happy you would be if you hadn't been hanged!"

The Commander dismissed the Negro slaves and the Paraguayans who were serving drinks in rock crystal goblets. He thanked God and St. Ignatius [5] a thousand times; he clasped Candide in his arms; their faces were bathed in tears. "You would be much more astonished, more touched, more beside yourself," said Candide, "if I told you that Mademoiselle Cunégonde, your sister, whom you thought disemboweled, is in good health." — "Where?" — "In your neighborhood, with Monsieur the Governor of Buenos Aires; and I was coming to make war on you." Every word they spoke in that long conversation piled wonder upon wonder. Their very soul flew from their tongues, was attentive in their ears, and sparkled in their eyes. Since they were Germans, they stayed at table for a long time, waiting for the Reverend Provincial Father; and this is how the Commander spoke to his dear Candide.

Chapitre Quinzième

Comment Candide Tua le Frère de Sa Chère Cunégonde

"J'aurai toute ma vie présent à la mémoire le jour horrible où je vis tuer mon père et ma mère, et violer ma sœur. Quand les Bulgares furent retirés, on ne trouva point cette sœur adorable, et on mit dans une charrette ma mère, mon père, et moi, deux servantes et trois petits garçons égorgés, pour nous aller enterrer dans une chapelle de jésuites, à deux lieues du château de mes pères. Un jésuite nous jeta de l'eau bénite; elle était horriblement salée; il en entra quelques gouttes dans mes yeux: le père s'aperçut que ma paupière faisait un petit mouvement: il mit la main sur mon cœur et le sentit palpiter; je fus secouru, et au bout de trois semaines il n'y paraissait pas. Vous savez, mon cher Candide, que j'étais fort joli, je le devins encore davantage; aussi le révérend père Croust,[1] supérieur de la maison, prit pour moi la plus tendre amitié: il me

[1] Voltaire's rancor was tenacious. In the early editions, the name is "Didrie," a made-up name. Croust refers to Father Antoine Croust, who was rector of Colmar from 1753 to 1763.

Fifteenth Chapter

How Candide Killed His Dear Cunégonde's Brother

"All my life I shall retain in my memory the horrible day when I saw my father and mother killed and my sister raped. When the Bulgarians were withdrawn, that adorable sister could not be found, and my mother, my father, and I, two servant girls, and three little butchered boys were put into a cart to be taken to be buried in a Jesuit chapel, five miles from the country house of my ancestors. A Jesuit threw holy water on us; it was horribly salty; several drops of it fell into my eyes; the Father noticed that my eyelids made a little movement; he put his hand on my heart, and felt it palpitating; I was rescued, and at the end of three weeks all was well. You know, my dear Candide, that I was very pretty; I became even more so, so the Reverend Father Croust,[1] superior of the house, conceived the most tender friendship for me; he gave

Voltaire had run afoul of him during his stay at Colmar in 1754. Voltaire's sly hint at possible homosexual leanings was one of his favorite devices.

donna l'habit de novice; quelque temps après je fus envoyé à Rome. Le père général avait besoin d'une recrue de jeunes jésuites allemands. Les souverains du Paraguai reçoivent le moins qu'ils peuvent de jésuites espagnols; ils aiment mieux les étrangers, dont ils se croient plus maîtres. Je fus jugé propre par le révérend père général pour aller travailler dans cette vigne.[2] Nous partîmes, un Polonais, un Tyrolien, et moi. Je fus honoré, en arrivant, du sous-diaconat et d'une lieutenance; je suis aujourd'hui colonel et prêtre. Nous recevons vigoureusement les troupes du roi d'Espagne; je vous réponds qu'elles seront excommuniées et battues. La Providence vous envoie ici pour nous seconder. Mais est-il bien vrai que ma chère sœur Cunégonde soit dans le voisinage, chez le gouverneur de Buenos-Ayres?" Candide l'assura par serment que rien n'était plus vrai. Leurs larmes recommencèrent à couler.

Le baron ne pouvait se lasser d'embrasser Candide; il l'appelait son frère, son sauveur. "Ah! peut-être, lui dit-il, nous pourrons ensemble, mon cher Candide, entrer en vainqueurs dans la ville et reprendre ma sœur Cunégonde. — C'est tout ce que je souhaite, dit Candide; car je comptais l'épouser, et je l'espère encore. — Vous, insolent! répondit le baron, vous auriez l'impudence d'épouser ma sœur, qui a soixante et douze quartiers! Je vous trouve bien effronté d'oser me parler d'un dessein si téméraire!" Candide, pétrifié d'un tel discours, lui répondit: "Mon révérend père, tous les

2 See Gospel of St. Matthew, 20:1–7.

me the clothes of a novice; sometime later I was sent to Rome. The Father General had need of some young German Jesuit recruits. The sovereigns of Paraguay take as few Spanish Jesuits as they can; they prefer foreigners, whom they think they master better. I was judged fit by the Reverend Father General to go and work in this vineyard.[2] We departed, a Pole, a Tyrolian, and I. Upon arriving, I was honored with a subdeacon-ship and a lieutenancy; today I am colonel and priest. We shall give the King of Spain's troops a vigorous reception; I guarantee you that they will be excommu-nicated and beaten. Providence sends you here to help us. But is it really true that my dear sister Cunégonde is in the neighborhood with the governor of Buenos Aires?" Candide assured him on oath that nothing was truer. Their tears began to flow once more.

The Baron could not tire of embracing Candide; he called him his brother, his savior. "Ah! Perhaps," he said to him, "we, my dear Candide, can together enter the city as victors, and retake my sister Cuné-gonde." — "That's all I hope for," said Candide; "for I was counting on marrying her, and I am still hoping for it." — "You, insolent fellow!" replied the Baron, "You would have the impudence of marrying my sis-ter, who has seventy-two quarterings! I find it extremely impudent that you dare speak to me of such a rash plan!" Candide, petrified at such a speech, replied: "My Reverend Father, all the quarterings in the world

quartiers du monde n'y font rien; j'ai tiré votre sœur des bras d'un juif et d'un inquisiteur, elle m'a assez d'obligations, elle veut m'épouser. Maître Pangloss m'a toujours dit que les hommes sont égaux, et assurément je l'épouserai. — C'est ce que nous verrons, coquin!" dit le jésuite baron de Thunder-ten-tronckh; et en même temps il lui donna un grand coup du plat de son épée sur le visage. Candide dans l'instant tire la sienne et l'enfonce jusqu'à la garde dans le ventre du baron jésuite; mais, en la retirant toute fumante, il se mit à pleurer: "Hélas! mon Dieu, dit-il, j'ai tué mon ancien maître, mon ami, mon beau-frère; je suis le meilleur homme du monde, et voilà déjà trois hommes que je tue, et dans ces trois il y a deux prêtres."

Cacambo, qui faisait sentinelle à la porte de la feuillée, accourut. "Il ne nous reste qu'à vendre cher notre vie, lui dit son maître; on va sans doute entrer dans la feuillée, il faut mourir les armes à la main." Cacambo, qui en avait bien vu d'autres, ne perdit point la tête; il prit la robe de jésuite que portait le baron, la mit sur le corps de Candide, lui donna le bonnet carré du mort, et le fit monter à cheval. Tout cela se fit en un clin d'œil. "Galopons, mon maître; tout le monde vous prendra pour un jésuite qui va donner des ordres; et nous aurons passé les frontières avant qu'on puisse courir après nous." Il volait déjà en prononçant ces paroles, et en criant en espagnol: "Place, place pour le révérend père colonel!"

make no difference; I have rescued your sister from the arms of a Jew and an Inquisitor; she has plenty of obligations to me, she wants to marry me. Master Pangloss always told me that men are equal; and certainly I will marry her." — "We'll see about that, rascal!" said the Jesuit Baron of Thunder-ten-tronckh; and at the same time he struck him a great blow on the face with the flat of his sword. Instantly Candide draws his, and plunges it into the belly of the Jesuit Baron up to the hilt; but in drawing it out all smoking he began to cry: "Alas! My God," he said, "I have killed my former master, my friend, my brother-in-law; I am the best-tempered man in the world, and here I have killed three men; and of those three two are priests."

Cacambo, who had been standing watch at the door of the arbor, came running. "There is nothing left for us but to sell our lives dearly," his master said to him; "doubtless they will be coming into the arbor; we must die arms in hand." Cacambo, who had seen much of this sort of thing before, did not lose his head; he took the Jesuit's robe the Baron was wearing, put it over Candide's body, gave him the dead man's square bonnet, and made him mount his horse. All this was done in the twinkling of an eye. "Let's gallop, my master; everybody will take you for a Jesuit on his way to give orders; and we will have passed the border before they can run after us." He was already fleeing when he spoke these words, and shouted in Spanish: "Way, make way for the Reverend Father Colonel!"

Chapitre Seizième

Ce Qui Advint aux Deux Voyageurs avec Deux Filles, Deux Singes, et les Sauvages Nommés Oreillons

Candide et son valet furent au delà des barrières, et personne ne savait encore dans le camp la mort du jésuite allemand. Le vigilant Cacambo avait eu soin de remplir sa valise de pain, de chocolat, de jambon, de fruit, et de quelques mesures de vin. Ils s'enfoncèrent avec leurs chevaux andalous dans un pays inconnu, où ils ne découvrirent aucune route. Enfin une belle prairie entrecoupée de ruisseaux se présenta devant eux. Nos deux voyageurs font repaître leurs montures. Cacambo propose à son maître de manger, et lui en donne l'exemple. "Comment veux-tu, disait Candide, que je mange du jambon, quand j'ai tué le fils de monsieur le baron, et que je me vois condamné à ne revoir la belle Cunégonde de ma vie? A quoi me servira de prolonger mes misérables jours, puisque je dois les traîner loin d'elle dans les remords et dans le désespoir? Et que dira le Journal de Trévoux?" [1]

[1] The celebrated Jesuit journal, founded in 1701. It ceased publication in 1775. Voltaire made merciless fun of it, but in

Sixteenth Chapter

What Happened to the Two Travelers with Two Girls, Two Monkeys, and the Savages Called Oreillons

Candide and his valet were beyond the barriers and no one in the camp yet knew of the death of the German Jesuit. The vigilant Cacambo had taken care to refill his bag with bread, chocolate, ham, fruits, and several bottles of wine. On their Andalusian horses they plunged into an unknown country where they discovered no road whatever. At last a beautiful prairie crosscut by streams appeared before them. Our two travelers fed their mounts. Cacambo suggests to his master that they eat, and sets him an example. "How do you expect me to eat ham," said Candide, "when I have killed the son of Monsieur the Baron, and when I see myself condemned not to see the beautiful Cunégonde as long as I live? What good will it do me to prolong my miserable days, since I must drag them out far from her in remorse and despair? And what will the *Journal de Trévoux* [1] say?"

fact it was an informative and usually scrupulously fair journal that specialized in long reviews of new scientific, philosophical, and theological works.

En parlant ainsi, il ne laissa pas de manger. Le soleil se couchait. Les deux égarés entendirent quelques petits cris qui paraissaient poussés par des femmes. Ils ne savaient si ces cris étaient de douleur ou de joie; mais ils se levèrent précipitamment avec cette inquiétude et cette alarme que tout inspire dans un pays inconnu. Ces clameurs partaient de deux filles toutes nues qui couraient légèrement au bord de la prairie, tandis que deux singes les suivaient en leur mordant les fesses. Candide fut touché de pitié; il avait appris à tirer chez les Bulgares, et il aurait abattu une noisette dans un buisson sans toucher aux feuilles. Il prend son fusil espagnol à deux coups, tire, et tue les deux singes. "Dieu soit loué, mon cher Cacambo! j'ai délivré d'un grand péril ces deux pauvres créatures: si j'ai commis un péché en tuant un inquisiteur et un jésuite, je l'ai bien réparé en sauvant la vie à deux filles. Ce sont peut-être deux demoiselles de condition, et cette aventure nous peut procurer de très grands avantages dans le pays."

Il allait continuer, mais sa langue devint percluse quand il vit ces deux filles embrasser tendrement les deux singes, fondre en larmes sur leurs corps, et remplir l'air des cris les plus douloureux. "Je ne m'attendais pas à tant de bonté d'âme," dit-il enfin à Cacambo, lequel lui répliqua: "Vous avez fait là un beau chef-d'œuvre, mon maître; vous avez tué les deux amants de ces demoiselles. — Leurs amants! serait-il possible? vous vous moquez de moi, Cacambo; le moyen de vous croire? — Mon cher maître, repartit Cacambo,

128

While speaking this way, he did not fail to eat. The sun was setting. The two wanderers heard several little cries which seemed to be uttered by women. They did not know whether these cries were of pain or of joy; but they arose hastily with that anxiety and alarm which everything inspires in an unknown country. These clamors came from two stark naked girls, who were running lightly along the edge of the prairie, while two monkeys followed them biting their behinds. Candide was moved by pity; among the Bulgarians he had learned to shoot, and he could have knocked down a nut from a bush without touching the leaves. He takes his double-barreled Spanish rifle, shoots, and kills the two monkeys. "God be praised, my dear Cacambo! I have delivered these two poor creatures from a great peril; if I have committed a sin in killing an Inquisitor and a Jesuit, I have thoroughly made it up by saving the lives of two girls. These are perhaps two young ladies of quality, and this adventure may secure us great advantages in this country."

He was about to go on, but his tongue was paralyzed when he saw these two girls tenderly embrace the two monkeys, burst into tears over their bodies, and fill the air with the most pitiful cries. "I had not expected so much goodness of soul," he finally said to Cacambo; who replied: "You have performed a masterpiece there, my master; you have killed the two lovers of these ladies." — "Their lovers! Can it be possible? You are making fun of me, Cacambo; how can I believe you?" — "My dear master," returned Cacambo,

129

vous êtes toujours étonné de tout; pourquoi trouvez-vous si étrange que dans quelques pays il y ait des singes qui obtiennent les bonnes grâces des dames? Ils sont des quarts d'homme, comme je suis un quart d'Espagnol. — Hélas! reprit Candide, je me souviens d'avoir entendu dire à maître Pangloss qu'autrefois pareils accidents étaient arrivés, et que ces mélanges avaient produit des égypans, des faunes, des satyres; que plusieurs grands personnages de l'antiquité en avaient vu; mais je prenais cela pour des fables.[2] — Vous devez être convaincu à présent, dit Cacambo, que c'est une vérité, et vous voyez comment en usent les personnes qui n'ont pas reçu une certaine éducation; tout ce que je crains, c'est que ces dames ne nous fassent quelque méchante affaire."

Ces réflexions solides engagèrent Candide à quitter la prairie et à s'enfoncer dans un bois. Il y soupa avec Cacambo; et tous deux, après avoir maudit l'inquisiteur de Portugal, le gouverneur de Buenos-Ayres et le baron, s'endormirent sur de la mousse. A leur réveil, ils sentirent qu'ils ne pouvaient remuer: la raison en était que pendant la nuit les Oreillons,[3] habitants du pays, à qui les deux dames les avaient dénoncés, les avaient garrottés avec des cordes d'écorce d'arbre. Ils étaient entourés d'une cinquantaine d'Oreillons tout

[2] Voltaire took these "fables" and the claim that there were ancients who had actually seen satyrs from the abbé Banier's *La mythologie et les fables expliquées par l'Histoire* (edition of 1740). The book has a chapter on "Satyrs, Faunes et Egipans."

"you're always astonished at everything; why do you find it so strange that in some countries there should be monkeys who obtain ladies' favors? They are one-quarter men just as I am one-quarter Spanish." — "Alas!" returned Candide, "I remember hearing Master Panglcss say that in earlier times similar accidents had happened and that these mixtures had produced Aigypans, fauns, satyrs; that many great personages of antiquity had seen them; but I had taken this for fables." [2] — "Now you ought to be convinced," said Cacambo, "that it is the truth, and you see how people behave who have not received a certain education; all I fear is that these ladies may get us into trouble."

These solid reflections led Candide to leave the prairie and to plunge into the woods. There he dined with Cacambo; and the two, after they had cursed the Inquisitor of Portugal, the governor of Buenos Aires, and the Baron, fell asleep on moss. When they woke up, they found that they could not move; the reason for that was that during the night, the Oreillons,[3] the inhabitants of the country, to whom the two ladies had denounced them, had tied them up with cords made of bark. They were surrounded by about fifty

[3] The name is derived from the Spanish word *"orejones,"*—big ears. This tribe of South American Indians got that name for its custom of piercing its ears for the sake of hanging wooden ornaments from their ear lobes. The whole incident sounds like a reminiscence of *Gulliver's Travels*.

nus, armés de flèches, de massues, et de haches de caillou: les uns faisaient bouillir une grande chaudière; les autres préparaient des broches, et tous criaient: "C'est un jésuite, c'est un jésuite! nous serons vengés, et nous ferons bonne chère; mangeons du jésuite, mangeons du jésuite!"

"Je vous l'avais bien dit, mon cher maître, s'écria tristement Cacambo, que ces deux filles nous joueraient d'un mauvais tour." Candide, apercevant la chaudière et les broches, s'écria: "Nous allons certainement être rôtis ou bouillis. Ah! que dirait maître Pangloss, s'il voyait comme la pure nature est faite? [4] Tout est bien, soit; mais j'avoue qu'il est bien cruel d'avoir perdu Mademoiselle Cunégonde et d'être mis à la broche par des Oreillons." Cacambo ne perdait jamais la tête. "Ne désespérez de rien, dit-il au désolé Candide; j'entends un peu le jargon de ces peuples, je vais leur parler. — Ne manquez pas, dit Candide, de leur représenter quelle est l'inhumanité affreuse de faire cuire des hommes, et combien cela est peu chrétien."

"Messieurs, dit Cacambo, vous comptez donc manger aujourd'hui un jésuite? C'est très bien fait; rien n'est plus juste que de traiter ainsi ses ennemis. En effet le droit naturel nous enseigne à tuer notre prochain, et c'est ainsi qu'on en agit dans toute la terre. Si nous n'usons pas du droit de le manger, c'est que nous avons d'ailleurs de quoi faire bonne chère; mais vous

[4] Voltaire's "*la pure nature*" is an allusion to the "state of nature," the pre-political state of man which was a commonplace

stark naked Oreillons, armed with arrows, clubs, and stone hatchets; some were bringing a big cauldron to a boil, others were preparing spits, and all shouted: "It's a Jesuit, it's a Jesuit! We'll be avenged, and we'll eat well; let's eat Jesuit, let's eat Jesuit!"

"I told you, my dear master," Cacambo sadly exclaimed, "that these two girls would play us a bad trick." Candide, seeing the cauldron and the spits, exclaimed: "We're surely going to be roasted or boiled. Ah! What would Master Pangloss say, if he saw how pure nature is made?[4] All is well; granted; but I confess that it is very cruel to have lost Mademoiselle Cunégonde and to be put on the spit by Oreillons." Cacambo never lost his head. "Don't despair of anything," he said to the disconsolate Candide; "I understand a little of the jargon of this nation, I'll talk to them." — "Don't fail to point out to them," said Candide, "what dreadful inhumanity it is to cook men, and how un-Christian it is."

"Gentlemen," said Cacambo, "so you're counting on eating a Jesuit today? Well done; nothing is juster than to treat your enemies this way. In fact natural law teaches us to kill our neighbor, and this is how everyone acts everywhere. If we don't exercise the right of eating him, that's because we have other things to make a good meal with; but you don't have the same re-

in the speculations of seventeenth and eighteenth-century political theorists.

n'avez pas les mêmes ressources que nous: certainement il vaut mieux manger ses ennemis que d'abandonner aux corbeaux et aux corneilles le fruit de sa victoire.[5] Mais, Messieurs, vous ne voudriez pas manger vos amis. Vous croyez aller mettre un jésuite en broche, et c'est votre défenseur, c'est l'ennemi de vos ennemis que vous allez rôtir. Pour moi, je suis né dans votre pays; monsieur que vous voyez est mon maître, et, bien loin d'être jésuite, il vient de tuer un jésuite, il en porte les dépouilles: voilà le sujet de votre méprise. Pour vérifier ce que je vous dis, prenez sa robe, portez-la à la première barrière du royaume de Los Padres; informez-vous si mon maître n'a pas tué un officier jésuite. Il vous faudra peu de temps; vous pourrez toujours nous manger, si vous trouvez que je vous ai menti. Mais, si je vous ai dit la vérité, vous connaissez trop les principes du droit public, les mœurs et les lois, pour ne nous pas faire grâce."

Les Oreillons trouvèrent ce discours très raisonnable; ils députèrent deux notables pour aller en diligence s'informer de la vérité; les deux députés s'acquittèrent de leur commission en gens d'esprit, et revinrent bientôt apporter de bonnes nouvelles. Les Oreillons délièrent leurs deux prisonniers, leur firent toutes sortes de civilités, leur offrirent des filles, leur donnèrent des rafraîchissements, et les reconduisirent jusqu'aux confins de leurs États, en criant avec allégresse: "Il n'est point jésuite, il n'est point jésuite!"

[5] It is evident from the article "Antropofages" in the *Dic-*

sources as we do; certainly it is better to eat your enemy than to abandon the fruits of your victory to crows and ravens.[5] But, gentlemen, you would not want to eat your friends. You think you're about to put a Jesuit on a spit, and it is your defender, it is the enemy of your enemies whom you are about to roast. As for myself, I was born in your country; the gentleman you see is my master, and far from being a Jesuit, he has just killed a Jesuit, he is wearing his spoils; that's the reason for your misunderstanding. To confirm what I am telling you, take his robe, carry it to the first barrier of the kingdom of Los Padres and find out if my master has not killed a Jesuit officer. It will take you little time; you can still eat us if you have found I have lied to you. But if I have told you the truth, you know the principles of international law, its uses and regulations too well, not to pardon us."

The Oreillons found this speech very reasonable; they deputized two notables to go with speed to discover the truth; the two deputies fulfilled their commission like men of intelligence, and soon returned bringing the good news. The Oreillons untied their two prisoners, paid them all kind of courtesies, offered them girls, gave them refreshments, and guided them all the way to the borders of their state, shouting with joy: "He's not a Jesuit, he's not a Jesuit!"

tionnaire philosophique that Cacambo is expressing Voltaire's own views here.

135

Candide ne se lassait point d'admirer le sujet de sa délivrance. "Quel peuple! disait-il, quels hommes! quelles mœurs! Si je n'avais pas eu le bonheur de donner un grand coup d'épée au travers du corps du frère de Mademoiselle Cunégonde, j'étais mangé sans rémission. Mais, après tout, la pure nature est bonne, puisque ces gens-ci, au lieu de me manger, m'ont fait mille honnêtetés dès qu'ils ont su que je n'étais pas jésuite."

Candide did not cease wondering at the reason for his deliverance. "What a nation!" he said. "What men! What customs! If I had not had the good luck of giving a big sword thrust through the body of Mademoiselle Cunégonde's brother I would have been eaten without mercy. But after all pure nature is good, because these people here, instead of eating me, have given me a thousand courtesies as soon as they found out that I was not a Jesuit."

Chapitre Dix-septième

Arrivée de Candide et de Son Valet au Pays d'Eldorado,[1] et ce Qu'Ils y Virent

Quand ils furent aux frontières des Oreillons: "Vous voyez, dit Cacambo à Candide, que cet hémisphère-ci ne vaut pas mieux que l'autre; croyez-moi, retournons en Europe par le plus court. — Comment y retourner, dit Candide, et où aller? Si je vais dans mon pays, les Bulgares et les Abares y égorgent tout; si je retourne en Portugal, j'y suis brûlé; si nous restons dans ce pays-ci, nous risquons à tout moment d'être mis en broche. Mais comment se résoudre à quitter la partie du monde que Mademoiselle Cunégonde habite?"

"Tournons vers la Cayenne, dit Cacambo: nous y trouverons des Français, qui vont par tout le monde; ils pourront nous aider. Dieu aura peut-être pitié de nous."

Il n'était pas facile d'aller à la Cayenne: ils savaient bien à peu près de quel côté il fallait marcher; mais des montagnes, des fleuves, des précipices, des brigands, des sauvages, étaient partout de terribles obstacles.

[1] As Voltaire himself explains in Chapter 18 (p. 151), the name for this fabulous country comes from the Spanish "el

Seventeenth Chapter

Arrival of Candide and His Valet in the Land of El Dorado,[1] and What They Saw There

When they were at the frontiers of the Oreillons, Cacambo said to Candide: "You see that this hemisphere is no better than the other; believe me, let's go back to Europe as fast as possible." — "How can we get back there," said Candide, "and where are we to go? If I go to my country, the Bulgarians and the Abarians are slaughtering everybody there; if I return to Portugal, I am burned; if we stay in this country we risk being put on the spit at any moment. But how can we bring ourselves to leave the part of the world inhabited by Mademoiselle Cunégonde?"

"Let's head toward Cayenne," said Cacambo, "there we will find Frenchmen, who go all across the world; they could help us. Perhaps God will have pity on us."

It was not easy to go to Cayenne; they knew pretty well just what direction they had to go; but mountains, rivers, precipices, brigands, savages, were terrible obstacles everywhere. Their horses died of fatigue; their

dorado"—the golden. Its existence had been seriously accepted in the sixteenth century, but by the eighteenth century it was mainly a general name for a Utopia.

Leurs chevaux moururent de fatigue; leurs provisions furent consumées; ils se nourrirent un mois entier de fruits sauvages, et se trouvèrent enfin auprès d'une petite rivière bordée de cocotiers, qui soutinrent leur vie et leurs espérances.

Cacambo, qui donnait toujours d'aussi bons conseils que la vieille, dit à Candide: "Nous n'en pouvons plus, nous avons assez marché; j'aperçois un canot vide sur le rivage, emplissons-le de cocos, jetons-nous dans cette petite barque, laissons-nous aller au courant; une rivière mène toujours à quelque endroit habité. Si nous ne trouvons pas des choses agréables, nous trouverons du moins des choses nouvelles. — Allons, dit Candide, recommandons-nous à la Providence."

Ils voguèrent quelques lieues entre des bords tantôt fleuris, tantôt arides, tantôt unis, tantôt escarpés. La rivière s'élargissait toujours; enfin elle se perdait sous une voûte de rochers épouvantables qui s'élevaient jusqu'au ciel. Les deux voyageurs eurent la hardiesse de s'abandonner aux flots sous cette voûte. Le fleuve, resserré en cet endroit, les porta avec une rapidité et un bruit horrible. Au bout de vingt-quatre heures ils revirent le jour; mais leur canot se fracassa contre les écueils; il fallut se traîner de rocher en rocher pendant une lieue entière; enfin ils découvrirent un horizon immense, bordé de montagnes inaccessibles. Le pays était cultivé pour le plaisir comme pour le besoin; partout l'utile était agréable.[2] Les chemins étaient cou-

[2] A characteristic mixture of self-revelation, reminiscence, and classical allusion. In his letter of 24 May 1750, Frederick the Great had likened Voltaire to Horace for "joining the useful to

provisions were eaten up; they lived for a whole month on wild fruits, and at last found themselves near a little river bordered with cocoanut trees, which sustained their lives and their hopes.

Cacambo, who continued to give as good advice as the old woman, said to Candide: "We can't go on, we have walked enough, I notice an empty canoe on the river bank, let's fill it with cocoanuts, let's throw ourselves into this little boat, let's drift with the current; a river always leads to some inhabited place. If we don't find any pleasant things, we will at least find new things." — "Let's go," said Candide, "let us commit ourselves to providence."

They drifted several miles between banks, sometimes flowery, sometimes bare, sometimes hilly, sometimes flat. The river kept widening; at last it disappeared under an arch of terrible rocks that rose up to the heavens. The two travelers had the courage to abandon themselves to the waters under this arch. The stream narrowed at this point, and carried them with horrible rapidity and noise. After twenty-four hours they again saw the light, but their canoe crashed against the reefs; they had to drag themselves from rock to rock for several miles; finally they discovered an immense horizon, bordered by inaccessible mountains. The country was cultivated for pleasure as for need; everywhere the useful was agreeable.[2] The roads were

the agreeable." Actually Horace had written (*Ars poetica*, 343–4): *omne tulit punctum qui miscuit utile dulci*—he who has blended the useful with the agreeable has won every vote.

verts ou plutôt ornés de voitures d'une forme et d'une matière brillante, portant des hommes et des femmes d'une beauté singulière, traînés rapidement par de gros moutons rouges qui surpassaient en vitesse les plus beaux chevaux d'Andalousie, de Tétuan et de Méquinez.[3]

"Voilà pourtant, dit Candide, un pays qui vaut mieux que la Vestphalie." Il mit pied à terre avec Cacambo auprès du premier village qu'il rencontra. Quelques enfants du village, couverts de brocarts d'or tout déchirés, jouaient au palet à l'entrée du bourg; nos deux hommes de l'autre monde s'amusèrent à les regarder: leurs palets étaient d'assez larges pièces rondes, jaunes, rouges, vertes, qui jetaient un éclat singulier. Il prit envie aux voyageurs d'en ramasser quelques-uns; c'était de l'or, c'était des émeraudes, des rubis, dont le moindre aurait été le plus grand ornement du trône du Mogol. "Sans doute, dit Cacambo, ces enfants sont les fils du roi du pays qui jouent au petit palet." Le magister du village parut dans ce moment pour les faire rentrer à l'école. "Voilà, dit Candide, le précepteur de la famille royale."

Les petits gueux quittèrent aussitôt le jeu, en laissant à terre leurs palets et tout ce qui avait servi à leurs divertissements. Candide les ramasse, court au précepteur, et les lui présente humblement, lui faisant entendre par signes que Leurs Altesses royales avaient oublié leur or et leurs pierreries. Le magister du village,

[3] Two towns in Morocco.

covered, or rather ornamented, by carriages of a brilliant shape and material, bearing men and women of singular beauty, rapidly drawn by fat red sheep which surpassed in speed the handsomest horses of Andalusia, Tetuan, and Mequinez.[3]

"Here anyhow," said Candide, "is a country that is better than Westphalia." With Cacambo he set foot on land near the first village he encountered. Several village children, covered with tattered gold brocade, were playing quoits at the entrance to the village; our two men from the other world took pleasure in watching them; their quoits were rather large round pieces, yellow, red, green, which gave forth a singular lustre. The travelers got the idea of picking up several of them; they were gold, they were emeralds, rubies, the least of which would have been the largest ornament of the Mogul's throne.

"Doubtless," said Cacambo, "these children are the sons of the King of the country who are playing quoits." The village schoolmaster appeared at this moment to make them return to school. "Here," said Candide, "is the tutor of the royal family."

The little beggars left their game right away, and left the quoits on the ground and everything that had served for their amusement. Candide picks them up, runs to the tutor, and humbly presents them to him, giving him to understand by signs that their Royal Highnesses had forgotten their gold and their precious

en souriant, les jeta par terre, regarda un moment la figure de Candide avec beaucoup de surprise, et continua son chemin.

Les voyageurs ne manquèrent pas de ramasser l'or, les rubis, et les émeraudes. "Où sommes-nous? s'écria Candide; il faut que les enfants des rois de ce pays soient bien élevés, puisqu'on leur apprend à mépriser l'or et les pierreries." Cacambo était aussi surpris que Candide. Ils approchèrent enfin de la première maison du village; elle était bâtie comme un palais d'Europe. Une foule de monde s'empressait à la porte, et encore plus dans le logis; une musique très agréable se faisait entendre, et une odeur délicieuse de cuisine se faisait sentir. Cacambo s'approcha de la porte, et entendit qu'on parlait péruvien; c'était sa langue maternelle: car tout le monde sait que Cacambo était né au Tucuman, dans un village où l'on ne connaissait que cette langue. "Je vous servirai d'interprète, dit-il à Candide; entrons, c'est ici un cabaret."

Aussitôt deux garçons et deux filles de l'hôtellerie, vêtus de drap d'or, et les cheveux renoués avec des rubans, les invitent à se mettre à la table de l'hôte. On servit quatre potages garnis chacun de deux perroquets, un contour bouilli qui pesait deux cents livres, deux singes rôtis d'un goût excellent, trois cents colibris dans un plat, et six cents oiseaux-mouches dans un autre; des ragoûts exquis, des pâtisseries délicieuses; le tout dans des plats d'une espèce de cristal de roche. Les garçons et les filles de l'hôtellerie versaient plusieurs liqueurs faites de canne de sucre.

stones. The village schoolmaster, smiling, threw them on the ground and looked at Candide's face for a moment with much surprise, and continued on his way.

The travelers did not fail to pick up the gold, the rubies, and the emeralds. "Where are we?" exclaimed Candide. "The King's children must be well brought up in this country, for they are taught to despise gold and precious stones." Cacambo was as surprised as Candide. At last they approached the first house of the village; it was built like a palace in Europe. A crowd of people was flocking around the door, and even more inside the dwelling; very pleasant music could be heard and a delicious odor of cooking could be smelled. Cacambo approached the door, and heard that they were speaking Peruvian; that was his mother tongue; for everybody knows that Cacambo was born in Tucuman, in a village where one knew that language only. "I'll serve as your interpreter," he said to Candide, "let's enter, this is an inn."

Immediately two boys and two girls of the hostelry, dressed in cloth of gold, their hair bound with ribbons, invited them to sit at the host's table. They served four soups each garnished with two parakeets, a boiled condor that weighed two hundred pounds, two roast monkeys of excellent flavor, three hundred colibris on one platter, and six hundred hummingbirds on another; exquisite ragouts, and delicious pastries; all on platters of a kind of rock crystal. The boys and girls of the hostelry poured out several liqueurs made of sugarcane.

Les convives étaient pour la plupart des marchands et des voituriers, tous d'une politesse extrême, qui firent quelques questions à Cacambo avec la discrétion la plus circonspecte, et qui répondirent aux siennes d'une manière à le satisfaire.

Quand le repas fut fini, Cacambo crut, ainsi que Candide, bien payer son écot en jetant sur la table de l'hôte deux de ces larges pièces d'or qu'il avait ramassées; l'hôte et l'hôtesse éclatèrent de rire, et se tinrent longtemps les côtés. Enfin ils se remirent. "Messieurs, dit l'hôte, nous voyons bien que vous êtes des étrangers; nous ne sommes pas accoutumés à en voir. Pardonnez-nous si nous nous sommes mis à rire quand vous nous avez offert en payement les cailloux de nos grands chemins. Vous n'avez pas sans doute de la monnaie du pays, mais il n'est pas nécessaire d'en avoir pour dîner ici. Toutes les hôtelleries établies pour la commodité du commerce sont payées par le gouvernement. Vous avez fait mauvaise chère ici, parce que c'est un pauvre village; mais partout ailleurs vous serez reçus comme vous méritez de l'être." Cacambo expliquait à Candide tous les discours de l'hôte, et Candide les écoutait avec la même admiration et le même égarement que son ami Cacambo les rendait. "Quel est donc ce pays, disaient-ils l'un et l'autre, inconnu à tout le reste de la terre, et où toute la nature est d'une espèce si différente de la nôtre? C'est probablement le pays où tout va bien: car il faut absolument qu'il y en ait un de cette espèce. Et, quoi qu'en dît maître Pangloss, je me suis souvent aperçu que tout allait assez mal en Vestphalie."

For the most part the guests were merchants and coachmen, all of extreme politeness, who addressed several questions to Cacambo with a most circumspect discretion, and who replied to his questions in a manner calculated to satisfy him.

When the meal was finished, Cacambo, just like Candide, thought to pay his share by throwing on the host's table two of those large gold pieces which he had picked up; the host and hostess burst out laughing, and for a long time held their sides. At last they recovered. "Gentlemen," said the host, "we easily see that you are foreigners; we are not accustomed to seeing any. Forgive us if we started to laugh when you offered in payment the pebbles of our highways. Doubtless you have no money from this country, but it is not necessary to have any in order to dine here. All the hostelries established for the convenience of commerce are maintained by the government. You had a bad meal here, because it's a poor village; but everywhere else you will be received as you deserve to be."

Cacambo explained to Candide all the host's remarks, and Candide listened to them with the same wonder and same bewilderment with which his friend Cacambo offered them. "What, then, is this country," they said to one another, "unknown to the rest of the world, where all of nature is of a kind so different from ours? Probably this is the country where all is well; for there must absolutely be one of this kind. And, no matter what Master Pangloss said about it, I have often noticed that everything was pretty bad in Westphalia."

Chapitre Dix-huitième

Ce Qu'Ils Virent dans le Pays d'Eldorado

Cacambo témoigna à son hôte toute sa curiosité; l'hôte lui dit: "Je suis fort ignorant, et je m'en trouve bien; mais nous avons ici un vieillard retiré de la cour, qui est le plus savant homme du royaume, et le plus communicatif." Aussitôt il mène Cacambo chez le vieillard. Candide ne jouait plus que le second personnage, et accompagnait son valet. Ils entrèrent dans une maison fort simple, car la porte n'était que d'argent, et les lambris des appartements n'étaient que d'or, mais travaillés avec tant de goût que les plus riches lambris ne l'effaçaient pas. L'antichambre n'était à la vérité incrusté que de rubis et d'émeraudes; mais l'ordre dans lequel tout était arrangé réparait bien cette extrême simplicité.

Le vieillard reçut les deux étrangers sur un sofa matelassé de plumes de colibri, et leur fit présenter des liqueurs dans des vases de diamant; après quoi il satisfit à leur curiosité en ces termes:

"Je suis âgé de cent soixante et douze ans, et j'ai appris de feu mon père, écuyer du roi, les étonnantes

Eighteenth Chapter

What They Saw in the Land of El Dorado

Cacambo let his host see all of his curiosity. The host told him: "I am very ignorant, and I am doing very well; but we have here an old man retired from court who is the most learned man in the kingdom and the most communicative." Right away he takes Cacambo to the old man. Candide was now playing only a secondary part, and accompanied his valet. They entered a very simple house, for the door was only of silver, and the paneling in the apartments was only of gold, but carved with such taste that the richest paneling did not efface it. To be sure, the antechamber was only encrusted with rubies and emeralds, but the order in which everything was arranged quite made up for this extreme simplicity.

The old man received the two foreigners on a sofa stuffed with colibri feathers, and offered them liqueurs in diamond vessels; after which he satisfied their curiosity as follows:

"I am a hundred and seventy-two years old, and I learned from my late father, squire to the King, the

révolutions du Pérou dont il avait été témoin. Le royaume où nous sommes est l'ancienne patrie des Incas, qui en sortirent très imprudemment pour aller subjuguer une partie du monde, et qui furent enfin détruits par les Espagnols. Les princes de leur famille que restèrent dans leur pays natal furent plus sages; ils ordonnèrent, du consentement de la nation, qu'aucun habitant ne sortirait jamais de notre petit royaume; et c'est ce qui nous a conservé notre innocence et notre félicité. Les Espagnols ont une connaissance confuse de ce pays, ils l'ont appelé Eldorado, et un Anglais, nommé le chevalier Raleigh,[1] en a même approché il y a environ cent années; mais, comme nous sommes entourés de rochers inabordables et de précipices, nous avons toujours été jusqu'à présent à l'abri de la rapacité des nations de l'Europe, qui ont une fureur inconcevable pour les cailloux et pour la fange de notre terre, et qui, pour en avoir, nous tueraient tous jusqu'au dernier."

La conversation fut longue; elle roula sur la forme du gouvernement, sur les mœurs, sur les femmes, sur les spectacles publics, sur les arts. Enfin Candide, qui avait toujours du goût pour la métaphysique, fit demander par Cacambo si dans le pays il y avait une religion.

Le vieillard rougit un peu. "Comment donc! dit-il; en pouvez-vous douter? Est-ce que vous nous prenez pour des ingrats?" Cacambo demanda humblement quelle était la religion d'Eldorado. Le vieillard rougit

[1] Sir Walter Raleigh (1552–1618) was one of those who be-

astonishing revolutions of Peru of which he had been a witness. The kingdom in which we are is the ancient homeland of the Incas, who left it very imprudently to go and subjugate a part of the world and who were at last destroyed by the Spaniards. The princes of their family who stayed in their native land were wiser; they ordained, with the consent of the nation, that no inhabitant should ever leave our little kingdom; and that is what has preserved our innocence and felicity for us. The Spaniards had some confused knowledge of this country, they called it *El Dorado*; and an Englishman called Sir Raleigh [1] even approached it about a hundred years ago; but, since we are surrounded by such inaccessible rocks and precipices, we have so far been completely sheltered from the rapacity of the nations of Europe, who have an inconceivable lust for the pebbles and the mud of our country, and who in order to get it would kill us all, down to the last man."

The conversation was long; it touched on the form of government, on customs, on women, on public spectacles, on the arts. Finally Candide, who always had a taste for metaphysics, asked, through Cacambo, if there was a religion in the country.

The old man blushed a little. "Really!" he said; "can you doubt it? Do you take us for ingrates?" Cacambo humbly asked what was the religion of El Dorado. The old man blushed once more. "Can there be two re-

lieved in Eldorado and actually traveled to South America in 1595 to look for it. He returned to write a book on the *Discovery of Guiana* (1596), which Voltaire knew in a French version.

encore. "Est-ce qu'il peut y avoir deux religions? dit-il; nous avons, je crois, la religion de tout le monde; nous adorons Dieu du soir jusqu'au matin. — N'adorez-vous qu'un seul Dieu? dit Cacambo, qui servait toujours d'interprète aux doutes de Candide. — Apparemment, dit le vieillard, qu'il n'y en a ni deux, ni trois, ni quatre. Je vous avoue que les gens de votre monde font des questions bien singulières." Candide ne se lassait pas de faire interroger ce bon vieillard; il voulut savoir comment on priait Dieu dans l'Eldorado. "Nous ne le prions point, dit le bon et respectable sage; nous n'avons rien à lui demander; il nous a donné tout ce qu'il nous faut; nous le remercions sans cesse." [2] Candide eut la curiosité de voir des prêtres; il fit demander où ils étaient. Le bon vieillard sourit. "Mes amis, dit-il, nous sommes tous prêtres; le roi et tous les chefs de famille chantent des cantiques d'actions de grâces solennellement tous les matins; et cinq ou six mille musiciens les accompagnent. — Quoi! vous n'avez point de moines qui enseignent, qui disputent, qui gouvernent, qui cabalent, et qui font brûler les gens qui ne sont pas de leur avis? — Il faudrait que nous fussions fous, dit le vieillard; nous sommes tous ici du même avis, et nous n'entendons pas ce que vous voulez dire avec vos moines." Candide à tous ces discours demeurait en extase, et disait en lui-même: "Ceci est bien différent de la Vestphalie et du château de monsieur le baron:

[2] This whole passage is a brief, superficial exposition of Voltaire's deism: the half-religious, half-philosophical view that

ligions?" he said. "We have, I believe, the religion of all men; we worship God from evening until morning." — "Do you worship only one single God?" said Cacambo, who continued to serve as interpreter to Candide's doubts. — "Apparently," said the old man, "there aren't two, nor three, nor four. I confess that the people of your world ask very odd questions." Candide did not tire of having this good old man questioned; he wanted to know how they prayed to God in El Dorado. "We don't pray to Him," said the good and respectable sage; "we have nothing to ask of Him, He has given us everything we need; we thank Him without cease." [2] Candide was curious to see some priests; he inquired where they were. The good old man smiled. "My friend," he said, "we are all priests; the king and all the heads of families solemnly sing hymns of thanksgiving every morning, and five or six thousand musicians accompany them." — "What! You don't have monks who teach, quarrel, govern, intrigue, and have people burned who are not of their opinion?" — "We would have to be crazy," said the old man; "we are all of the same opinion here, and we don't understand what you are talking about with your monks." During all these remarks, Candide remained in ecstasy, and said to himself, "This is very different from Westphalia and the country house of Monsieur the

there is one God, creator of the universe, who rules the world by unchangeable, universal laws, neither rewards nor punishes, but gives man the reason with which he understands the moral law.

153

si notre ami Pangloss avait vu Eldorado, il n'aurait plus dit que le château de Thunder-ten-tronckh était ce qu'il y avait de mieux sur la terre; il est certain qu'il faut voyager."

Après cette longue conversation, le bon vieillard fit atteler un carrosse à six moutons, et donna douze de ses domestiques aux deux voyageurs pour les conduire à la cour. "Excusez-moi, leur dit-il, si mon âge me prive de l'honneur de vous accompagner. Le roi vous recevra d'une manière dont vous ne serez pas mécontents, et vous pardonnerez sans doute aux usages du pays, s'il y en a quelques-uns qui vous déplaisent."

Candide et Cacambo montent en carrosse; les six moutons volaient, et en moins de quatre heures on arriva au palais du roi, situé à un bout de la capitale. Le portail était de deux cent vingt pieds de haut et de cent de large; il est impossible d'exprimer quelle en était la matière. On voit assez quelle supériorité prodigieuse elle devait avoir sur ces cailloux et sur ce sable que nous nommons or et pierreries.

Vingt belles filles de la garde reçurent Candide et Cacambo à la descente du carrosse, les conduisirent aux bains, les vêtirent de robes d'un tissu de duvet de colibri; après quoi les grands officiers et les grandes officières de la couronne les menèrent à l'appartement de Sa Majesté au milieu de deux files, chacune de mille musiciens, selon l'usage ordinaire. Quand ils approchèrent de la salle du trône, Cacambo demanda à un grand officier comment il fallait s'y prendre pour saluer Sa Majesté: si on se jetait à genoux ou ventre à terre;

Baron; if our friend Pangloss had seen El Dorado, he would no longer have said that the country house of Thunder-ten-tronckh was the best there was on earth; it is certain that one must travel."

After this long conversation, the good old man had a carriage harnessed with six sheep and gave the two travelers twelve of his servants to conduct them to court. "Excuse me," he said to them, "if my age deprives me of the honor of accompanying you. The king will receive you in a manner that won't discontent you, and you will doubtless pardon the customs of the country, if there are some that displease you."

Candide and Cacambo climbed into the carriage; the six sheep flew, and in less than four hours they arrived at the palace of the king, situated at one end of the capital. The portal was two hundred and twenty feet high, and a hundred wide; it is impossible to explain what its material was. It is easy to see what prodigious superiority it must have had over those pebbles and sand that we call gold and precious stones.

Twenty beautiful girls of the Guard received Candide and Cacambo as they descended from the carriage, took them to the baths, dressed them in robes woven from colibri down; after which the grand lords and ladies of the crown led them to His Majesty's apartment between two files of a thousand musicians each, according to the common custom. When they approached the throne room, Cacambo asked a lord how they should go about saluting His Majesty; should they throw themselves on their knees or belly, should

si on mettait les mains sur la tête ou sur le derrière; si on léchait la poussière de la salle; en un mot, quelle était la cérémonie. "L'usage, dit le grand officier, est d'embrasser le roi et de le baiser des deux côtés." Candide et Cacambo sautèrent au cou de Sa Majesté, qui les reçut avec toute la grâce imaginable et qui les pria poliment à souper.

En attendant, on leur fit voir la ville, les édifices publics élevés jusqu'aux nues, les marchés ornés de mille colonnes, les fontaines d'eau pure, les fontaines d'eau rose, celles de liqueurs de canne de sucre qui coulaient continuellement dans de grandes places, pavées d'une espéce de pierreries qui répandaient une odeur semblable à celle du gérofle et de la cannelle. Candide demanda à voir la cour de justice, le parlement;[3] on lui dit qu'il n'y en avait point, et qu'on ne plaidait jamais. Il s'informa s'il y avait des prisons, et on lui dit que non. Ce qui le surprit davantage, et qui lui fit le plus de plaisir, ce fut le palais des sciences, dans lequel il vit une galerie de deux mille pas, toute pleine d'instruments de mathématique et de physique.[4]

Après avoir parcouru toute l'après-dînée à peu près la millième partie de la ville, on les ramena chez le roi. Candide se mit à table entre Sa Majesté, son valet

[3] "*Parlement*" is the French term for courts of law. In Voltaire's time, France had a dozen of these, the main one being in Paris. The French *parlements*, in addition to settling cases, claimed the right to participate in legislation by registering royal edicts and "remonstrating" against edicts they found unacceptable. Voltaire considered these claims both invalid in law and

they put their hands on their heads or on their be-
hinds; should they lick the dust of the room; in a word,
what was the ceremony? "The custom," said the lord,
"is to embrace the king and kiss him on both cheeks."
Candide and Cacambo threw their arms around the
neck of His Majesty, who received them with all the
grace imaginable, and politely asked them to supper.

While waiting, they were shown the town, the public
buildings raised up the clouds, the markets adorned
with a thousand columns, the fountains of pure water,
the fountains of rose water, those of cane sugar li-
queurs, which ran continually in great squares paved
with a kind of precious stone which emitted an odor
similar to that of cloves and cinnamon. Candide asked
to see the court of justice, the *parlement*; [3] he was told
that there wasn't one, and that nobody ever went to
law. He inquired if there were any prisons, and he was
told no. What surprised him even more, and gave him
the greatest pleasure, was the palace of sciences, in
which there was a gallery two thousand feet long, all
full of instruments of mathematics and physics. [4]

After they had spent all afternoon looking over about
a thousandth part of the city, they were taken back
to the king. Candide placed himself at table between

reactionary in politics, and supported the royal party through-
out his life.

[4] Unlike some other philosophers, Voltaire appreciated the role
of mathematics in science. While this Palace of Sciences sounds
a little like Bacon's *New Atlantis*, it is different in its stress on
mathematics.

Cacambo, et plusieurs dames. Jamais on ne fit meilleure chère, et jamais on n'eut plus d'esprit à souper qu'en eut Sa Majesté. Cacambo expliquait les bons mots du roi à Candide, et, quoique traduits, ils paraissaient toujours des bons mots. De tout ce qui étonnait Candide, ce n'était pas ce qui l'étonna le moins.

Ils passèrent un mois dans cet hospice. Candide ne cessait de dire à Cacambo: "Il est vrai, mon ami, encore une fois, que le château où je suis né ne vaut pas le pays où nous sommes; mais enfin Mademoiselle Cunégonde n'y est pas, et vous avez sans doute quelque maîtresse en Europe. Si nous restons ici, nous n'y serons que comme les autres; au lieu que si nous retournons dans notre monde seulement avec douze moutons chargés de cailloux d'Eldorado, nous serons plus riches que tous le rois ensemble, nous n'aurons plus d'inquisiteurs à craindre, et nous pourrons aisément reprendre Mademoiselle Cunégonde."

Ce discours plut à Cacambo: on aime tant à courir, à se faire valoir chez les siens, à faire parade de ce qu'on a vu dans ses voyages, que les deux heureux résolurent de ne plus l'être, et de demander leur congé à Sa Majesté.

"Vous faites une sottise, leur dit le roi; je sais bien que mon pays est peu de chose; mais, quand on est passablement quelque part, il faut y rester; je n'ai pas assurément le droit de retenir des étrangers; c'est une tyrannie qui n'est ni dans nos mœurs, ni dans nos lois: tous les hommes sont libres; partez quand vous voudrez, mais la sortie est bien difficile. Il est impossible

His Majesty, his valet Cacambo, and several ladies. Never did anyone eat better, and never was anyone wittier at supper than His Majesty. Cacambo explained the king's witticisms to Candide, and even in translation they continued to appear witty. Of everything that astonished Candide, this did not astonish him the least.

They spent a month in this refuge. Candide never stopped saying to Cacambo: "It is true, my friend, once again, that the country house where I was born can't be compared to the country where we are; but after all Mademoiselle Cunégonde is not here, and doubtless you have a mistress in Europe. If we stay here, we will only be like the others; whereas, if we return to our world merely with twelve sheep laden with pebbles of El Dorado, we shall be richer than all the kings put together; we'll no longer have Inquisitors to fear, and we'll easily be able to recover Mademoiselle Cunégonde."

This observation pleased Cacambo; people so much enjoy running about, showing off before one's own friends, making a parade of what one has seen on one's travels, that the two happy men resolved not to be so any longer, and to ask His Majesty's permission to go.

"You are doing something foolish," the king told them; "I know very well that my country isn't much; but, when you are comfortable somewhere, you ought to stay there. Certainly I have no right to detain foreigners; that is a tyranny which is neither part of our custom nor of our laws; all men are free; leave whenever you want, but the way out is very difficult. It is im-

de remonter la rivière rapide sur laquelle vous êtes arrivés par miracle, et qui court sous des voûtes de rochers. Les montagnes qui entourent tout mon royaume ont dix mille pieds de hauteur, et sont droites comme des murailles: elles occupent chacune en largeur un espace de plus de dix lieues; on ne peut en descendre que par des précipices. Cependant, puisque vous voulez absolument partir, je vais donner ordre aux intendants des machines d'en faire une qui puisse vous transporter commodément. Quand on vous aura conduits au revers des montagnes, personne ne pourra vous accompagner: car mes sujets ont fait vœu de ne jamais sortir de leur enceinte, et ils sont trop sages pour rompre leur vœu. Demandez-moi d'ailleurs tout ce qu'il vous plaira. — Nous ne demandons à Votre Majesté, dit Cacambo, que quelques moutons chargés de vivres, de cailloux, et de la boue du pays." Le roi rit: "Je ne conçois pas, dit-il, quel goût vos gens d'Europe ont pour notre boue jaune; mais emportez-en tant que vous voudrez, et grand bien vous fasse."

Il donna l'ordre sur-le-champ à ses ingénieurs de faire une machine pour guinder ces deux hommes extraordinaires hors du royaume. Trois mille bons physiciens y travaillèrent; elle fut prête au bout de quinze jours, et ne coûta pas plus de vingt millions de livres sterling, monnaie du pays. On mit sur la machine Candide et Cacambo; il y avait deux grands moutons rouges sellés et bridés pour leur servir de monture quand ils auraient franchi les montagnes, vingt moutons de bât chargés de vivres, trente qui portaient des présents de ce que

possible to go back up the rapid river by which you arrived through a miracle, and which was under arches of rocks. The mountains which surround my whole kingdom are ten thousand feet high, and are straight as walls; they each occupy a space more than thirty miles wide; you can descend them only through precipices. However, since you absolutely want to leave, I shall give orders to the superintendents of machines to make one which can transport you comfortably. When you have been taken to the other side of the mountains, no one will be able to accompany you; for my subjects have taken the vow of never leaving their enclosure, and they are too wise to break their vow. Apart from that, ask of me anything you please." — "We ask nothing of Your Majesty," said Cacambo, "only a few sheep loaded with victuals, pebbles, and some mud of the country." The king laughed. "I don't understand," he said, "the liking you people of Europe have for our yellow mud; but take as much of it as you want, and may it do you much good."

Immediately he gave orders to the engineers to make a machine that would hoist these two extraordinary men outside the kingdom. Three thousand good physicists worked on it; it was ready at the end of two weeks, and did not cost more than twenty million pound sterling, in the country's money. They put Candide and Cacambo on the machine; there were two big red sheep saddled and bridled to serve them as mounts when they had cleared the mountains, twenty pack-sheep laden with victuals, thirty which bore presents

le pays a de plus curieux, et cinquante chargés d'or, de pierreries et de diamants. Le roi embrassa tendrement les deux vagabonds.

Ce fut un beau spectacle que leur départ, et la manière ingénieuse dont ils furent hissés, eux et leurs moutons, au haut des montagnes. Les physiciens prirent congé d'eux après les avoir mis en sûreté, et Candide n'eut plus d'autre désir et d'autre objet que d'aller présenter ses moutons à Mademoiselle Cunégonde. "Nous avons, dit-il, de quoi payer le gouverneur de Buenos-Ayres, si Mademoiselle Cunégonde peut être mise à prix. Marchons vers la Cayenne, embarquons-nous, et nous verrons ensuite quel royaume nous pourrons acheter."

of the most curious products of the country, and fifty laden with gold, precious stones, and diamonds. The king embraced the two vagabonds tenderly.

Their departure and the ingenious manner in which they were hoisted, they and their sheep, to the top of the mountains, was a fine spectacle. The physicists took leave of them after they had put them down safely, and Candide no longer had any other desire and object than to go and present his sheep to Mademoiselle Cunégonde. "We have enough," he said, "to pay the governor of Buenos Aires, if Mademoiselle Cunégonde can be ransomed. Let's march toward Cayenne, let's take ship, and then we'll see what kingdom we can buy."

Chapitre Dix-neuvième

Ce Qui Leur Arriva à Surinam, et Comment
Candide Fit Connaissance avec Martin

La première journée de nos deux voyageurs fut assez
agréable. Ils étaient encouragés par l'idée de se voir
possesseurs de plus de trésors que l'Asie, l'Europe et
l'Afrique n'en pouvaient rassembler. Candide, trans-
porté, écrivit le nom de Cunégonde sur les arbres.
A la seconde journée, deux de leurs moutons s'enfon-
cèrent dans des marais, et y furent abîmés avec leurs
charges; deux autres moutons moururent de fatigue
quelques jours après; sept ou huit périrent ensuite de
faim dans un désert; d'autres tombèrent au bout de
quelques jours dans des précipices. Enfin, après cent
jours de marche, il ne leur resta que deux moutons.
Candide dit à Cacambo: "Mon ami, vous voyez comme
les richesses de ce monde sont périssables; il n'y a rien
de solide que la vertu et le bonheur de revoir Made-
moiselle Cunégonde. — Je l'avoue, dit Cacambo; mais
il nous reste encore deux moutons avec plus de trésors
que n'en aura jamais le roi d'Espagne, et je vois de loin
une ville que je soupçonne être Surinam, appartenant

Nineteenth Chapter

What Happened to Them at Surinam, and How Candide Made the Acquaintance of Martin

Our two travelers' first day was fairly pleasant. They were encouraged by the idea of seeing themselves possessors of more treasures than Asia, Europe, and Africa could assemble. Candide, in rapture, wrote Cunégonde's name on the trees. On the second day two of their sheep plunged into some marshes and were swallowed up with their loads; two other sheep died of fatigue several days later; after that seven or eight perished from hunger in a desert; others fell into precipices several days after. At last, after a hundred days of travel, only two sheep remained. Candide said to Cacambo: "My friend, you see how the riches of this world are perishable; there is nothing solid but virtue and the happiness of seeing Mademoiselle Cunégonde again." — "I admit it," said Cacambo; "but we still have two sheep left with more treasures than the King of Spain will ever have; and I see from afar a city I suspect is Surinam, which belongs to the Dutch. We

aux Hollandais. Nous sommes au bout de nos peines et au commencement de notre félicité."

En approchant de la ville, ils rencontrèrent un nègre étendu par terre, n'ayant plus que la moitié de son habit, c'est-à-dire d'un caleçon de toile bleue; il manquait à ce pauvre homme la jambe gauche et la main droite. "Eh! mon Dieu! lui dit Candide en hollandais, que fais-tu là, mon ami, dans l'état horrible où je te vois? — J'attends mon maître, Monsieur Vanderdendur,[1] le fameux négociant, répondit le nègre. — Est-ce Monsieur Vanderdendur, dit Candide, qui t'a traité ainsi? — Oui, Monsieur, dit le nègre, c'est l'usage. On nous donne un caleçon de toile pour tout vêtement deux fois l'année. Quand nous travaillons aux sucreries, et que la meule nous attrape le doigt, on nous coupe la main; quand nous voulons nous enfuir, on nous coupe la jambe: je me suis trouvé dans les deux cas. C'est à ce prix que vous mangez du sucre en Europe. Cependant, lorsque ma mère me vendit dix écus patagons[2] sur la côte de Guinée, elle me disait: 'Mon cher enfant, bénis nos fétiches, adore-les toujours, ils te feront vivre heureux; tu as l'honneur d'être esclave de nos seigneurs les blancs, et tu fais par là la fortune de ton père et de ta mère.' Hélas! je ne sais pas si j'ai fait leur fortune, mais ils n'ont pas fait la mienne. Les chiens, les singes et les perroquets sont mille fois moins malheureux que nous; les fétiches hollandais qui m'ont converti me

[1] All the commentators agree that this cruel Dutchman is named after the Dutch publisher Van Duren, with whom Vol-

are at the end of our troubles and at the beginning of our happiness."

As they approached the city, they met a Negro stretched on the ground, with no more than half of his clothes, that is to say a pair of underpants of blue cotton; this poor man had his left leg and his right hand missing. "Oh! my God!" Candide said to him in Dutch, "what are you doing there, my friend, in the horrible condition I see you in?" — "I'm waiting for my master, Monsieur Vanderdendur,[1] the famous merchant," replied the Negro. — "Is it Monsieur Vanderdendur," said Candide, "who has treated you this way?" — "Yes, Monsieur," said the Negro, "it's the custom. They give us a pair of cotton pants for all our clothing twice a year. When we work in the sugar mills, and when our finger is caught in the grindstone, they cut off our hand; when we try to flee, they cut off a leg; I've been in both situations. This is the price at which you eat sugar in Europe. However, when my mother sold me on the Guinea coast for ten patacóns,[2] she said to me: 'My dear child, bless our fetishes, worship them always, they will make you live happily; you have the honor of being slave of our Lords the whites, and with this you are making your father's and mother's fortune.' Alas! I don't know if I made their fortune, but they didn't make mine. Dogs, monkeys, and parrots are a thousand times less miserable than

taire had had difficulties over the manuscript of Frederick the Great's *Anti-Machiavel* around 1740.

[2] A Portuguese (and Brazilian) silver coin.

disent tous les dimanches que nous sommes tous enfants d'Adam, blancs et noirs. Je ne suis pas généalogiste; mais si ces prêcheurs disent vrai, nous sommes tous cousins issus de germain. Or vous m'avouerez qu'on ne peut pas en user avec ses parents d'une manière plus horrible."

"O Pangloss! s'écria Candide, tu n'avais pas deviné cette abomination; c'en est fait, il faudra qu'à la fin je renonce à ton optimisme. — Qu'est-ce qu'optimisme? disait Cacambo. — Hélas! dit Candide, c'est la rage de soutenir que tout est bien quand on est mal"; et il versait des larmes en regardant son nègre; et, en pleurant, il entra dans Surinam.

La première chose dont ils s'informent, c'est s'il n'y a point au port quelque vaisseau qu'on pût envoyer à Buenos-Ayres. Celui à qui ils s'adressèrent était justement un patron espagnol, qui s'offrit à faire avec eux un marché honnête. Il leur donna rendez-vous dans un cabaret. Candide et le fidèle Cacambo allèrent l'y attendre avec leurs deux moutons.

Candide, qui avait le cœur sur les lèvres, conta à l'Espagnol toutes ses aventures, et lui avoua qu'il voulait enlever Mademoiselle Cunégonde. "Je me garderai bien de vous passer à Buenos-Ayres, dit le patron: je serais pendu, et vous aussi. La belle Cunégonde est la maîtresse favorite de monseigneur." Ce fut un coup de foudre pour Candide; il pleura longtemps; enfin il tira à part Cacambo: "Voici, mon cher ami, lui dit-il, ce qu'il faut que tu fasses. Nous avons chacun dans nos poches pour cinq ou six millions de diamants; tu es

we; the Dutch fetishes who have converted me tell me every Sunday that we are all Adam's children, black and white. I'm not a genealogist; but if these preachers are telling the truth, we are all second cousins. Now you'll admit to me that one cannot deal with one's relatives in a more horrible way."

"O Pangloss!" Candide exclaimed, "this abomination you had not guessed; that's too much, in the end I'll have to renounce your optimism." — "What is optimism?" said Cacambo. — "Alas!" said Candide, "it's the mania of maintaining that all is well when one is wretched"; and he shed tears looking at his Negro; and he entered Surinam weeping.

The first thing they inquired about was if there was not some ship in port that could be sent to Buenos Aires. The one to whom they addressed themselves proved to be a Spanish captain who offered to make an honest bargain with them. He suggested they meet at an inn. Candide and the faithful Cacambo went there to wait for him with their two sheep.

Candide, whose heart was on his lips, told the Spaniard all his adventures, and admitted to him that he wanted to carry off Mademoiselle Cunégonde. "I'll take good care not to transport you to Buenos Aires," said the captain; "I'd be hanged and you would be too; the beautiful Cunégonde is Monseigneur's favorite mistress." That was a thunderbolt for Candide, he wept for a long time; finally he took Cacambo aside. "Now, my dear friend," he said to him, "here's what you do. We each have in our pockets five or six millions' worth

plus habile que moi; va prendre Mademoiselle Cuné-
gonde à Buenos-Ayres. Si le gouverneur fait quelques
difficultés, donne-lui un million; s'il ne se rend pas,
donne-lui-en deux; tu n'as point tué d'inquisiteur, on
ne se défiera point de toi. J'équiperai un autre vais-
seau; j'irai t'attendre à Venise; c'est un pays libre où
l'on n'a rien à craindre ni des Bulgares, ni des Abares,
ni des juifs, ni des inquisiteurs." Cacambo applaudit
à cette sage résolution. Il était au désespoir de se
séparer d'un bon maître devenu son ami intime; mais
le plaisir de lui être utile l'emporta sur la douleur de le
quitter. Ils s'embrassèrent en versant des larmes: Can-
dide lui recommanda de ne point oublier la bonne
vieille. Cacambo partit dès le jour même: c'était un
très bon homme que ce Cacambo.

Candide resta encore quelque temps à Surinam, et
attendit qu'un autre patron voulût le mener en Italie,
lui et les deux moutons qui lui restaient. Il prit des
domestiques, et acheta tout ce qui lui était nécessaire
pour un long voyage; enfin Monsieur Vanderdendur,
maître d'un gros vaisseau, vint se présenter à lui. "Com-
bien voulez-vous, demanda-t-il à cet homme, pour me
mener en droiture à Venise, moi, mes gens, mon bagage,
et les deux moutons que voilà?" Le patron s'accorda à
dix mille piastres; Candide n'hésita pas.

"Oh! oh! dit à part soi le prudent Vanderdendur,
cet étranger donne dix mille piastres tout d'un coup!
il faut qu'il soit bien riche." Puis, revenant un moment
après, il signifia qu'il ne pouvait partir à moins de vingt
mille. "Eh bien! vous les aurez," dit Candide.

of diamonds; you are cleverer than I; go and get Mademoiselle Cunégonde in Buenos Aires. If the governor makes any difficulties, give him a million; if he doesn't give up, give him two; you haven't killed an Inquisitor, they won't mistrust you. I'll outfit another ship, I'll go and wait for you in Venice; that's a free country where there is nothing to fear either from Bulgarians, or Abarians, or Jews, or Inquisitors." Cacambo applauded this sage resolution. He was in despair at being separated from a good master who had become his intimate friend; but the pleasure of being useful to him overcame the pain of leaving him. They embraced, shedding tears; Candide advised him not to forget the good old woman. Cacambo left that very day; he was a very good man, this Cacambo.

Candide stayed in Surinam for some time more, and waited for another captain who would be willing to take him to Italy, him and the two sheep that remained. He took servants and bought all he needed for a long voyage; at last Monsieur Vanderdendur, master of the big ship, came to introduce himself. "How much do you want," he asked this man, "to take me straight to Venice, me, my people, my baggage, and the two sheep here?" The captain agreed on ten thousand piastres; Candide did not hesitate.

"Oh! Oh!" the prudent Vanderdendur said to himself, "this foreigner gives ten thousand piastres right off! He must be very rich." Then, coming back a moment later, he gave notice that he could not leave for less than twenty thousand piastres. "Oh! well, you'll have them," said Candide.

"Ouais! se dit tout bas le marchand, cet homme donne vingt mille piastres aussi aisément que dix mille." Il revint encore, et dit qu'il ne pouvait le conduire à Venise à moins de trente mille piastres. "Vous en aurez donc trente mille," répondit Candide.

"Oh! oh! se dit encore le marchand hollandais, trente mille piastres ne coûtent rien à cet homme-ci; sans doute les deux moutons portent des trésors immenses; n'insistons pas davantage: faisons-nous d'abord payer les trente mille piastres, et puis nous verrons." Candide vendit deux petits diamants, dont le moindre valait plus que tout l'argent que demandait le patron. Il le paya d'avance. Les deux moutons furent embarqués. Candide suivait dans un petit bateau pour joindre le vaisseau à la rade; le patron prend son temps, met à la voile, démarre; le vent le favorise. Candide, éperdu et stupéfait, le perd bientôt de vue. "Hélas! cria-t-il, voilà un tour digne de l'ancien monde." Il retourne au rivage, abîmé dans la douleur: car enfin il avait perdu de quoi faire la fortune de vingt monarques.

Il se transporte chez le juge hollandais; et, comme il était un peu troublé, il frappe rudement à la porte; il entre, expose son aventure, et crie un peu plus haut qu'il ne convenait. Le juge commença par lui faire payer dix mille piastres pour le bruit qu'il avait fait; ensuite il l'écouta patiemment, lui promit d'examiner son affaire sitôt que le marchand serait revenu, et se fit payer dix mille autres piastres pour les frais de l'audience.

"Wow!" the merchant said softly to himself, "this man gives twenty thousand piastres as easily as ten thousand." He came back once more, and said that he could not take him to Venice for less than thirty thousand piastres. "Then you shall have thirty thousand," replied Candide.

"Oh! Oh!" the Dutch merchant said to himself again, "thirty thousand piastres don't cost this man anything; doubtless the two sheep are carrying immense treasures; let's not insist any more; let's have those thirty thousand piastres paid first, and then we'll see." Candide sold two small diamonds, of which the smaller was worth more than all the money the captain was asking. He paid him in advance. The two sheep were put aboard. Candide followed in a little boat to join the ship in the roads. The captain takes this opportunity, sets sail, weighs anchor; the wind favors him. Candide, aghast and stupefied, soon loses sight of him. "Alas!" he cried, "here's a trick worthy of the old world." He returns to shore overwhelmed with grief; for after all he had lost enough to make the fortunes of twenty monarchs.

He goes to see the Dutch judge; and, since he was a little upset, he knocks loudly at the door; he enters, sets forth his adventure, and shouts a little more loudly than was suitable. The judge began by making him pay ten thousand piastres for the noise he had made; after that he listened to him patiently, promised him to examine his case as soon as the merchant had returned, and had himself paid ten thousand more piastres for the costs of the hearing.

Ce procédé acheva de désespérer Candide; il avait à la vérité essuyé des malheurs mille fois plus douloureux; mais le sang-froid du juge, et celui du patron dont il était volé, alluma sa bile, et le plongea dans une noire mélancolie. La méchanceté des hommes se présentait à son esprit dans toute sa laideur; il ne se nourrissait que d'idées tristes. Enfin un vaisseau français étant sur le point de partir pour Bordeaux, comme il n'avait plus de moutons chargés de diamants à embarquer, il loua une chambre du vaisseau à juste prix, et fit signifier dans la ville qu'il payerait le passage, la nourriture, et donnerait deux mille piastres à un honnête homme qui voudrait faire le voyage avec lui, à condition que cet homme serait le plus dégoûté de son état et le plus malheureux de la province.

Il se présenta une foule de prétendants qu'une flotte n'aurait pu contenir. Candide voulant choisir entre les plus apparents, il distingua une vingtaine de personnes qui lui paraissaient assez sociables, et qui toutes prétendaient mériter la préférence. Il les assembla dans son cabaret, et leur donna à souper, à condition que chacun ferait serment de raconter fidèlement son histoire, promettant de choisir celui qui lui paraîtrait le plus à plaindre et le plus mécontent de son état, à plus juste titre, et de donner aux autres quelques gratifications.

La séance dura jusqu'à quatre heures du matin. Candide, en écoutant toutes leurs aventures, se ressouvenait de ce que lui avait dit la vieille en allant à Buenos-Ayres, et de la gageure qu'elle avait faite, qu'il n'y

This procedure completed Candide's despairs; true, he had undergone miseries a thousand times more painful; but the judge's coldbloodedness, and that of the captain by whom he had been robbed, inflamed his bile, and plunged him into a black melancholy. The malice of men appeared to his mind in all its ugliness, he nourished himself with sad ideas alone. Finally, with a French vessel ready to depart for Bordeaux, since he no longer had sheep laden with diamonds to put on board, he hired a cabin of the ship at a reasonable price, and let it be known in the town that he would pay passage, food, and give two thousand piastres to an honest man who would want to take the trip with him, on condition that this man be the most disgusted with his lot, and the most unhappy man in the province.

A crowd of applicants presented itself that a fleet could not have contained. Candide, wanting to choose among the most likely, selected about twenty persons who seemed to him sociable enough, and who all claimed to deserve preference. He assembled them at his inn, and gave them supper, on condition that each would take an oath to tell his story faithfully, promising to choose the one who would seem to him to have the best reason for being the most to be pitied and the most discontented with his lot, and to give the others some gratuities.

The session lasted until four in the morning. Candide, listening to all the adventures, remembered what the old woman had said to him on the way to Buenos Aires, and the bet she had made that there was no one

avait personne sur le vaisseau à qui il ne fût arrivé de très grands malheurs. Il songeait à Pangloss à chaque aventure qu'on lui contait. "Ce Pangloss, disait-il, serait bien embarrassé à démontrer son système. Je voudrais qu'il fût ici. Certainement, si tout va bien, c'est dans Eldorado, et non pas dans le reste de la terre." Enfin il se détermina en faveur d'un pauvre savant qui avait travaillé dix ans pour les libraires à Amsterdam. Il jugea qu'il n'y avait point de métier au monde dont on dût être plus dégoûté.[3]

Ce savant, qui était d'ailleurs un bon homme, avait été volé par sa femme, battu par son fils, et abandonné de sa fille, qui s'était fait enlever par un Portugais. Il venait d'être privé d'un petit emploi duquel il subsistait; et les prédicants de Surinam le persécutaient parce qu'ils le prenaient pour un socinien.[4] Il faut avouer que les autres étaient pour le moins aussi malheureux que lui; mais Candide espérait que le savant le désennuierait dans le voyage. Tous ses autres rivaux trouvèrent que Candide leur faisait une grande injustice; mais il les apaisa en leur donnant à chacun cent piastres.

[3] Until he settled at Ferney, Voltaire had constant trouble with publishers: in an age of censorship, the rascally publisher flourished; Voltaire was a good property, and many of his books were pirated, bringing the publisher quick money and the author nothing. Here is a partial revenge.

[4] Follower of Faustus Socinus (1539–1604) and his uncle Laelius Socinus (1525–62), two heretical Italian philosophers who spent much of their lives in exile. They were antitrini-

on the ship to whom very great misfortunes had not happened. With each adventure he was being told he thought of Pangloss. "This Pangloss," he said, "would be much embarrassed to demonstrate his system. I wish he were here. Certainly, if all is well, it is in El Dorado and not in the rest of the world." Finally he made up his mind in favor of a poor scholar who had worked ten years for the booksellers of Amsterdam. He decided that there was no occupation in the world one should be more disgusted with.[3]

This scholar, who was a good man besides, had been robbed by his wife, beaten by his son, and abandoned by his daughter, who had had herself carried off by a Portuguese. He had just been deprived of a small job on which he subsisted; and the preachers of Surinam persecuted him because they took him for a Socinian.[4] It must be admitted that the others were at least as miserable as he; but Candide hoped that the scholar would divert him on the trip. All his other rivals thought that Candide was doing them a great injustice; but he appeased them by giving each of them a hundred piastres.

tarians (and hence the ancestors of the Unitarians), and optimistic about man's goodness and rationality (and hence the ancestors of deism). Voltaire was convinced that his friends among the Genevan clergy were Socinians, and had told d'Alembert the same thing. Unfortunately, d'Alembert broadcast the news in his article on "Genève" in the *Encyclopédie,* and thus caused much uproar.

Chapitre Vingtième

Ce Qui Arriva sur Mer à Candide et à Martin

Le vieux savant, qui s'appelait Martin, s'embarqua donc pour Bordeaux avec Candide. L'un et l'autre avaient beaucoup vu et beaucoup souffert; et quand le vaisseau aurait dû faire voile de Surinam au Japon par le cap de Bonne-Espérance, ils auraient eu de quoi s'entretenir du mal moral et du mal physique pendant tout le voyage.

Cependant Candide avait un grand avantage sur Martin, c'est qu'il espérait toujours revoir Mademoiselle Cunégonde, et que Martin n'avait rien à espérer; [1] de plus, il avait de l'or et des diamants; et, quoiqu'il eût perdu cent gros moutons rouges chargés des plus grands trésors de la terre, quoiqu'il eût toujours sur le cœur la friponnerie du patron hollandais, cependant, quand il songeait à ce qui lui restait dans ses poches, et quand il parlait de Cunégonde, surtout à la fin du repas, il penchait alors pour le système de Pangloss.

[1] A visible sign of the connection of *Candide* with the *Poème sur le désastre de Lisbonne*, which ends with the line: "But we might still add hope"—to our grim sense of loss and failure in

Twentieth Chapter

What Happened to Candide and Martin at Sea

So the old scholar, who was called Martin, embarked with Candide for Bordeaux. Both of them had seen much and had suffered much; and if the ship should have set sail from Surinam to Japan by the Cape of Good Hope, they would have had enough to discuss about the moral evil and physical evil for the whole voyage.

However, Candide had a great advantage over Martin, which is that he continued to hope to see Mademoiselle Cunégonde again, and Martin had nothing to hope for; [1] moreover he had gold and diamonds; and even though he had lost a hundred big red sheep laden with the greatest treasures on earth, even though he had the Dutch captain's rascality on his mind, nevertheless, when he thought of what remained in his pockets, and when he spoke of Cunégonde, especially at the end of a meal, he still inclined toward Pangloss' system.

this world. It is evident that for Voltaire, hope was a slim reed; work, as we shall see in the last chapter of *Candide*, is far stronger.

"Mais vous, Monsieur Martin, dit-il au savant, que pensez-vous de tout cela? Quelle est votre idée sur le mal moral et le mal physique? — Monsieur, répondit Martin, mes prêtres m'ont accusé d'être socinien; mais la vérité du fait est que je suis manichéen.[2] — Vous vous moquez de moi, dit Candide, il n'y a plus de manichéens dans le monde. — Il y a moi, dit Martin; je ne sais qu'y faire, mais je ne peux penser autrement. — Il faut que vous ayez le diable au corps, dit Candide. — Il se mêle si fort des affaires de ce monde, dit Martin, qu'il pourrait bien être dans mon corps, comme partout ailleurs; mais je vous avoue qu'en jetant la vue sur ce globe, ou plutôt sur ce globule, je pense que Dieu l'a abandonné à quelque être malfaisant; j'en excepte toujours Eldorado. Je n'ai guère vu de ville qui ne désirât la ruine de la ville voisine, point de famille qui ne voulût exterminer quelque autre famille. Partout les faibles ont en exécration les puissants devant lesquels ils rampent, et les puissants les traitent comme des troupeaux dont on vend la laine et la chair. Un million d'assassins enrégimentés, courant d'un bout de l'Europe à l'autre, exerce le meurtre et le brigandage avec discipline pour gagner son pain, parce qu'il n'a pas de métier plus honnête; et dans les villes qui paraissent jouir de la paix, et où les arts fleurissent, les hommes sont dévorés de plus d'envie, de soins et d'inquiétudes

[2] Follower of the third-century Persian visionary Mani or Manes, whose doctrine offered rather serious competition to early Christianity. Manicheanism teaches the coexistence of two in-

"But you, Monsieur Martin," he said to the scholar, "what do you think of all that? What is your idea on moral evil and physical evil?" — "Monsieur," replied Martin, "my priest accused me of being a Socinian; but the truth of the matter is that I am a Manichean." [2] — "You're making fun of me," said Candide, "there are no Manicheans left in the world." — "There's me," said Martin; "I don't know what to do about it, but I can't think any other way." — "You must be possessed by the devil," said Candide. — "He takes part so much in the affairs of this world," said Martin, "that he might well be in my body, as everywhere else; but I admit to you that in casting my eye over this globe, or rather this globule, I think that God has abandoned it to some maleficent being; El Dorado always excepted. I have hardly seen a town that did not desire the ruin of the neighboring town, nor a family which did not want to exterminate some other family. Everywhere the weak hold in execration the powerful before whom they cower and the powerful treat them like flocks whose wool and flesh they sell. A million enlisted assassins, running from one end of Europe to the other, practice murder and robbery in perfect discipline to earn their bread, because there is no more honest trade; and in the towns that seem to enjoy peace and where the arts flourish, men are devoured by more

dependent principles, one good, one evil, which are in eternal combat. Its doctrines were frequently mistaken for those of the Socinians, a mistake against which Bayle had already protested.

qu'une ville assiégée n'éprouve de fléaux. Les chagrins secrets sont encore plus cruels que les misères publiques. En un mot, j'en ai tant vu et tant éprouvé que je suis manichéen. — Il y a pourtant du bon, répliquait Candide. — Cela peut être, disait Martin, mais je ne le connais pas."

Au milieu de cette dispute, on entendit un bruit de canon. Le bruit redouble de moment en moment. Chacun prend sa lunette. On aperçoit deux vaisseaux qui combattaient à la distance d'environ trois milles; le vent les amena l'un et l'autre si près du vaisseau français qu'on eut le plaisir de voir le combat tout à son aise. Enfin l'un des deux vaisseaux lâcha à l'autre une bordée si bas et si juste qu'il le coula à fond. Candide et Martin aperçurent distinctement une centaine d'hommes sur le tillac du vaisseau qui s'enfonçait; ils levaient tous les mains au ciel et jetaient des clameurs effroyables: en un moment tout fut englouti.

"Eh bien! dit Martin, voilà comme les hommes se traitent les uns les autres. — Il est vrai, dit Candide, qu'il y a quelque chose de diabolique dans cette affaire." En parlant ainsi, il aperçut je ne sais quoi d'un rouge éclatant qui nageait auprès de son vaisseau. On détacha la chaloupe pour voir ce que ce pouvait être: c'était un de ses moutons. Candide eut plus de joie de retrouver ce mouton qu'il n'avait été affligé d'en perdre cent tous chargés de gros diamants d'Eldorado.

Le capitaine français aperçut bientôt que le capitaine du vaisseau submergeant était espagnol, et que celui du vaisseau submergé etait un pirate hollandais; c'était

envy, cares, and anxieties than the scourges suffered by a besieged city. Secret griefs are even more cruel than public miseries. In a word, I have seen so much and suffered so much that I am a Manichean." — "Still there is some good," replied Candide. — "That may be," said Martin; "but I don't know it."

In the midst of this dispute, the sound of cannon was heard. The noise redoubles from moment to moment. Everyone takes his spy glass and perceives two ships fighting one another about three miles away; the wind brought them so near the French ship that they had the pleasure of seeing the combat quite at their ease. At last one of the two ships launched a broadside at the other so low and so accurate as to sink it. Candide and Martin distinctly observed about a hundred men on the main deck of the sinking ship; they all lifted their hands to heaven and uttered dreadful screams; in a moment all was swallowed up.

"Well," said Martin, "this is how men treat one another." — "It is true," said Candide, "that there is something diabolical in this affair." As he was saying this, he noticed some bright red thing that was swimming near his ship. They lowered a little boat to see what it could be; it was one of his sheep. Candide had more joy in finding that sheep again than he had been afflicted by losing a hundred of them all laden with big diamonds from El Dorado.

The French captain soon noticed that the captain of the surviving ship was Spanish, and that the captain of the ship that had been sunk was a Dutch pirate; it

celui-là même qui avait volé Candide. Les richesses immenses dont ce scélérat s'était emparé furent ensevelies avec lui dans la mer, et il n'y eut qu'un mouton de sauvé. "Vous voyez, dit Candide à Martin, que le crime est puni quelquefois; ce coquin de patron hollandais a eu le sort qu'il méritait. — Oui, dit Martin; mais fallait-il que les passagers qui étaient sur son vaisseau périssent aussi? Dieu a puni ce fripon, le diable a noyé les autres."

Cependant le vaisseau français et l'espagnol continuèrent leur route, et Candide continua ses conversations avec Martin. Ils disputèrent quinze jours de suite, et au bout de quinze jours ils étaient aussi avancés que le premier. Mais enfin ils parlaient, ils se communiquaient des idées, ils se consolaient. Candide caressait son mouton. "Puisque je t'ai retrouvé, dit-il, je pourrai bien retrouver Cunégonde."

was the very same who had robbed Candide. The immense riches that this scoundrel had got hold of were buried with him in the sea, and nothing but one sheep was saved. "You see," said Candide to Martin, "that crime is sometimes punished; this rascal of a Dutch captain met the fate he deserved." — "Yes," said Martin; "but was it necessary for the passengers who were on his ship to perish too? God punished that scoundrel, the devil drowned the others."

Meanwhile the French ship and the Spanish continued their voyage, and Candide continued his conversation with Martin. They argued for two weeks together, and at the end of two weeks they were as far as they had been on the first day. But after all they were talking, they were exchanging ideas, they were consoling one another. Candide caressed his sheep. "Since I've found you again," he said, "I may well find Cunégonde again."

Chapitre Vingt-unième

Candide et Martin Approchent des Côtes de France, et Raisonnent

On aperçut enfin les côtes de France. "Avez-vous jamais été en France, Monsieur Martin? dit Candide. — Oui, dit Martin, j'ai parcouru plusieurs provinces. Il y en a où la moitié des habitants est folle, quelques-unes où l'on est trop rusé, d'autres où l'on est communément assez doux et assez bête, d'autres où l'on fait le bel esprit; et, dans toutes, la principale occupation est l'amour, la seconde de médire, et la troisième de dire des sottises. — Mais, Monsieur Martin, avez-vous vu Paris? — Oui, j'ai vu Paris; il tient de toutes ces espèces-là; c'est un chaos, c'est une presse dans laquelle tout le monde cherche le plaisir, et où presque personne ne le trouve, du moins à ce qu'il m'a paru. J'y ai séjourné peu; j'y fus volé, en arrivant, de tout ce que j'avais, par des filous, à la foire Saint-Germain; [1] on me prit moi-même pour un voleur; et je fus huit jours en prison; après quoi je me fis correcteur d'imprimerie

[1] This fair was an old and popular Parisian institution.

Twenty-first Chapter

Candide and Martin Approach the Coast of France and Argue

The coast of France was sighted at last. "Have you ever been to France, Monsieur Martin?" said Candide. — "Yes," said Martin, "I've traveled through several provinces. There are some where half of the inhabitants are mad, some where they are too subtle, others where they are generally fairly gentle and fairly stupid, others where they claim to be clever; and in all, the principal occupation is love; the second slander; and the third talking nonsense." — "But, Monsieur Martin, have you seen Paris?" — "Yes, I've seen Paris; it has something of all those species; it's a chaos, it's a crowd in which everybody seeks pleasure, and where almost no one finds it, at least so it seemed to me. I stayed there only briefly; when I got there, I was robbed of all I had by pickpockets at the Saint-Germain fair;[1] they took me for a thief myself, and I was in jail for a week; after which I turned printer's proofreader to earn

pour gagner de quoi retourner à pied en Hollande. Je connus la canaille écrivante, la canaille cabalante et la canaille convulsionnaire.[2] On dit qu'il y a des gens fort polis dans cette ville-là; je le veux croire."

"Pour moi, je n'ai nulle curiosité de voir la France, dit Candide; vous devinez aisément que, quand on a passé un mois dans Eldorado, on ne se soucie plus de rien voir sur la terre que Mademoiselle Cunégonde; je vais l'attendre à Venise; nous traverserons la France pour aller en Italie; ne m'accompagnerez-vous pas? — Très volontiers, dit Martin; on dit que Venise n'est bonne que pour les nobles vénitiens, mais que cependant on y reçoit très bien les étrangers quand ils ont beaucoup d'argent; je n'en ai point, vous en avez, je vous suivrai partout. — A propos, dit Candide, pensez-vous que la terre ait été originairement une mer, comme on l'assure dans ce gros livre qui appartient au capitaine du vaisseau? — Je n'en crois rien du tout, dit Martin, non plus que de toutes les rêveries qu'on nous débite depuis quelque temps.[3] — Mais à quelle fin ce monde a-t-il donc été formé? dit Candide. — Pour nous faire enrager, répondit Martin. — N'êtes-vous pas

[2] Voltaire is here alluding to an incident that took place in Paris in the late 1720's and early 1730's. A fervent Jansenist named Pâris (1690–1727), who lived a life of poverty and charity in Paris, was buried in the cemetery of St. Médard after his early death. His grave became the scene of wild outbursts of religious revivalism ("convulsions") and the demonstrators had to be dispersed by the police. Incidentally, *"canaille"* is one of Voltaire's favorite disparaging terms.

enough to return to Holland on foot. I came to know the writing canaille, the intriguing canaille, and the convulsionary canaille.[2] They say that there are some extremely polite people in that city; I'm willing to believe it."

"As for myself, I have no curiosity to see France," said Candide; "you can easily guess that when you've spent a month in El Dorado, you don't care to see anything else on earth except Mademoiselle Cunégonde; I shall wait for her in Venice; we will cross France to go to Italy; will you accompany me?" — "Very gladly," said Martin; "they say that Venice is good only for Venetian nobles, but, still, that they receive foreigners very well when they have a lot of money; I haven't; you have, I shall follow you everywhere." — "By the way," said Candide, "do you think that the earth was originally a sea, as it is claimed in that fat book that belonged to the ship's captain?" — "I believe nothing of the sort," said Martin, "any more than all the reveries they have been retailing for some time." [3] — "But to what end, then, was this world created?" said Candide. — "To drive us mad," replied Martin. — "Aren't

[3] Voltaire is referring to the continuing argument over the age and early character of the world. "That big book" in the preceding paragraph is probably the Bible, but Voltaire is also thinking of the *Théorie de la terre* (1749) by the great scientist Buffon (1707–88), which in this respect at least followed the Biblical account. Voltaire had a rather good-natured prolonged debate with Buffon on this subject.

bien étonné, continua Candide, de l'amour que ces deux filles du pays des Oreillons avaient pour ces deux singes, et dont je vous ai conté l'aventure? — Point du tout, dit Martin; je ne vois pas ce que cette passion a d'étrange; j'ai tant vu de choses extraordinaires qu'il n'y a plus rien d'extraordinaire. — Croyez-vous, dit Candide, que les hommes se soient toujours mutuellement massacrés comme ils font aujourd'hui? qu'ils aient toujours été menteurs, fourbes, perfides, ingrats, brigands, faibles, volages, lâches, envieux, gourmands, ivrognes, avares, ambitieux, sanguinaires, calomniateurs, débauchés, fanatiques, hypocrites et sots? — Croyez-vous, dit Martin, que les éperviers aient toujours mangé des pigeons quand ils en ont trouvé? — Oui, sans doute, dit Candide. — Eh bien! dit Martin, si les éperviers ont toujours eu le même caractère, pourquoi voulez-vous que les hommes aient changé le leur? — Oh! dit Candide, il y a bien de la différence, car le libre arbitre . . ." En raisonnant ainsi, ils arrivèrent à Bordeaux.

you very surprised," continued Candide, "at the love of those two girls in the land of the Oreillons for those two monkeys, whose adventures I told you about?" — "Not in the least," said Martin, "I don't see what is strange about that passion; I have seen so many extraordinary things that there is nothing extraordinary any more." — "Do you think," said Candide, "that men have always massacred each other as they are doing today? That they have always been liars, crooks, traitors, ingrates, brigands, weaklings, unreliables, cowards, enviers, gluttons, drunkards, misers, social climbers, bloodsuckers, slanderers, debauchees, fanatics, hypocrites, and fools?" — "Do you think," said Martin, "that sparrow hawks have always eaten pigeons when they found some?" — "Yes, without doubt," said Candide. — "All right!" said Martin, "if sparrow hawks have always had the same character, why do you expect men should have changed theirs?" — "Oh!" said Candide, "there is a great difference, for free will . . ." Arguing thus, they arrived at Bordeaux.

Chapitre Vingt-deuxième

Ce Qui Arriva en France à Candide et à Martin

Candide ne s'arrêta dans Bordeaux qu'autant de temps qu'il en fallait pour vendre quelques cailloux du Dorado, et pour s'accommoder d'une bonne chaise à deux places: car il ne pouvait plus se passer de son philosophe Martin; il fut seulement très fâché de se séparer de son mouton, qu'il laissa à l'Académie des sciences de Bordeaux,[1] laquelle proposa pour le sujet du prix de cette année de trouver pourquoi la laine de ce mouton était rouge; et le prix fut adjugé à un savant du Nord, qui démontra par A plus B, moins C, divisé par Z, que le mouton devait être rouge, et mourir de la clavelée.[2]

Cependant tous les voyageurs que Candide rencontra dans les cabarets de la route lui disaient: "Nous allons à Paris." Cet empressement général lui donna enfin l'envie de voir cette capitale; ce n'était pas beaucoup se détourner du chemin de Venise.

[1] Voltaire was an associate member of this academy; it was a custom among these academies to set prize questions annually.

Twenty-second Chapter

What Happened to Candide and Martin in France

Candide stopped in Bordeaux only long enough to sell some pebbles from El Dorado, and to provide himself with a good two-seated chaise; for he could no longer do without his philosopher Martin; only he was very sorry to part with his sheep, which he left with the Academy of Sciences of Bordeaux,[1] which offered as the subject of the prize of that year the question why the wool of this sheep was red; and the prize was awarded to a scholar from the North, who demonstrated by A plus B, minus C, divided by Z, that the sheep must be red and die of scab.[2]

Meanwhile all of the travelers Candide met in the inns on the road said to him: "We are going to Paris." This general eagerness finally gave him the desire to see this capital; it was not much out of the way from the road to Venice.

[2] An obvious hit at the fine French astronomer Maupertuis (1698–1758) with whom Voltaire had quarreled, and whose mathematical work (which was brilliant) he mercilessly ridiculed.

Il entra par le faubourg Saint-Marceau, et crut être dans le plus vilain village de la Vestphalie.[3]

A peine Candide fut-il dans son auberge qu'il fut attaqué d'une maladie légère causée par ses fatigues. Comme il avait au doigt un diamant énorme, et qu'on avait aperçu dans son équipage une cassette prodigieusement pesante, il eut aussitôt auprès de lui deux médecins qu'il n'avait pas mandés, quelques amis intimes qui ne le quittèrent pas, et deux dévotes qui faisaient chauffer ses bouillons. Martin disait: "Je me souviens d'avoir été malade à Paris dans mon premier voyage; j'étais fort pauvre: aussi n'eus-je ni amis, ni dévotes, ni médecins, et je guéris."

Cependant, à force de médecines et de saignées, la maladie de Candide devint sérieuse. Un habitué du quartier vint avec douceur lui demander un billet payable au porteur pour l'autre monde;[4] Candide n'en voulut rien faire. Les dévotes l'assurèrent que c'était une nouvelle mode; Candide répondit qu'il n'était point homme à la mode. Martin voulut jeter l'habitué par les fenêtres; le clerc jura qu'on n'enterrerait point Candide; Martin jura qu'il enterrerait le clerc s'il continuait à les importuner. La querelle s'échauffa; Martin le prit par les épaules, et le chassa rudement;

[3] Voltaire, who loved his native city even though he spent much of his life outside it, disliked some of its dirtier quarters, of which this *faubourg* was an example.

[4] A veiled allusion to the *billets de confession*, which divided religious Frenchmen in the late 1740's. As a check on the Jansenist minority in the church, the Archbishop of Paris had decreed in 1746 that no believer could obtain the sacraments

He entered by the Faubourg Saint-Marceau, and thought he was in the shabbiest village in Westphalia.[3]

Hardly was Candide in his inn when he was attacked by a slight illness, caused by his fatigue. Since he had an enormous diamond on his finger, and since a prodigiously heavy money box had been noticed in his baggage, he immediately had two physicians near him whom he had not called, some intimate friends who did not leave him, and two devout ladies who had his broths heated. Martin said: "I remember having been sick too in Paris on my first trip; I was very poor; so I had neither friends, nor devout ladies, nor doctors, and I got well."

However, thanks to medicines and bleedings, Candide's illness became serious. An unbeneficed priest of the neighborhood came and sweetly asked him for a note payable to the bearer in the other world;[4] Candide wanted nothing to do with it. The devout ladies assured him that this was a new fashion; Candide replied that he was not a man of fashion. Martin wanted to throw the priest out the window. The cleric swore that they would not bury Candide. Martin swore that he would bury the cleric if he continued to molest them. The quarrel grew heated; Martin took him by the shoulders, and rudely pushed him out; which caused

unless he had a *billet de confession*. This "note" proved that the believer had confessed to a priest who accepted the papal Bull Unigenitus, a Bull that severely censured Jansenist beliefs. The quarrel died down in the mid-1750's, but Voltaire continued to enjoy it.

ce qui causa un grand scandale, dont on fit un procès-verbal.

Candide guérit; et pendant sa convalescence il eut très bonne compagnie à souper chez lui. On jouait gros jeu. Candide était tout étonné que jamais les as ne lui vinssent; et Martin ne s'en étonnait pas.

Parmi ceux qui lui faisaient les honneurs de la ville, il y avait un petit abbé périgourdin, l'un de ces gens empressés, toujours alertes, toujours serviables, effrontés, caressants, accommodants, qui guettent les étrangers à leur passage, leur content l'histoire scandaleuse de la ville, et leur offrent des plaisirs à tout prix. Celui-ci mena d'abord Candide et Martin à la comédie. On y jouait une tragédie nouvelle. Candide se trouva placé auprès de quelques beaux esprits. Cela ne l'empêcha pas de pleurer à des scènes jouées parfaitement. Un des raisonneurs qui étaient à ses côtés lui dit dans un entr'acte: "Vous avez grand tort de pleurer: cette actrice est fort mauvaise; l'acteur qui joue avec elle est plus mauvais acteur encore; la pièce est encore plus mauvaise que les acteurs; l'auteur ne sait pas un mot d'arabe, et cependant la scène est en Arabie; et, de plus, c'est un homme qui ne croit pas aux idées innées: [5] je vous apporterai demain vingt brochures contre lui.[6] — Monsieur, combien avez-vous de pièces de théâtre en France?" dit Candide à l'abbé, lequel répondit: "Cinq ou six mille. — C'est beaucoup, dit Candide;

[5] That makes him a follower of John Locke (1632–1704), and thus in agreement with Voltaire.

a great scandal, on which an official report was made.

Candide got well; and during his convalescence, he had very good company to supper with him. They gambled for high stakes. Candide was greatly surprised that he never held any aces; and Martin was not surprised at this.

Among those who did the honors of the town for him was a little abbé from Périgord, one of those eager people, always alert, always obliging, brazen, fawning, accommodating, on the lookout for strangers passing through, telling scandalous tales of the town, and offering them pleasures at any price. This one first took Candide and Martin to the theater. They were performing a new tragedy there. Candide found himself placed next to some wits. This did not prevent him from crying at perfectly acted scenes. One of the logicians by his side said to him during intermission: "You are quite wrong to cry, this actress is very bad; and the actor acting with her is a still worse actor; and the piece is even worse than the actress; the author does not know a word of Arabic, and yet the scene is in Arabia; and what's more, he is a man who does not believe in innate ideas; [5] tomorrow I'll bring you twenty brochures against him." [6] — "Monsieur, how many theatrical pieces do you have in France?" said Candide to the others; who replied: "Five or six thousand." — "That's a lot," said Candide; "how

[6] Beginning at this point, and ending on p. 215, Voltaire inserted a long passage which first appeared in the edition of 1761.

combien y en a-t-il de bonnes? — Quinze ou seize, répliqua l'autre. — C'est beaucoup," dit Martin.

Candide fut très content d'une actrice qui faisait la reine Elisabeth dans une assez plate tragédie que l'on joue quelquefois.[7] "Cette actrice, dit-il à Martin, me plaît beaucoup; elle a un faux air de Mademoiselle Cunégonde; je serais bien aise de la saluer." L'abbé périgourdin s'offrit à l'introduire chez elle. Candide, élevé en Allemagne, demanda quelle était l'étiquette, et comment on traitait en France les reines d'Angleterre. "Il faut distinguer, dit l'abbé; en province, on les mène au cabaret; à Paris, on les respecte quand elles sont belles, et on les jette à la voirie quand elles sont mortes. — Des reines à la voirie! dit Candide. — Oui vraiment, dit Martin; monsieur l'abbé a raison: j'étais à Paris quand Mademoiselle Monime passa, comme on dit, de cette vie à l'autre; on lui refusa ce que ces gens-ci appellent *les honneurs de la sépulture*, c'est-à-dire de pourrir avec tous les gueux du quartier dans un vilain cimetière; elle fut enterrée toute seule de sa bande au coin de la rue de Bourgogne; ce qui dut lui faire une peine extrême, car elle pensait très noblement.[8] — Cela est bien impoli, dit Candide. — Que voulez-vous? dit

[7] *Le comte d'Essex*, by Thomas Corneille (1625–1709), younger brother of the great Pierre Corneille, whose plays Voltaire admired greatly.

[8] Voltaire's good friend Adrienne Lecouvreur (1690–1730), a great actress, was buried in unhallowed ground after her early death, a fate reserved for people of the theater. Voltaire wrote a moving poem on her death, *La mort de Mlle Lecouvreur,*

many of them are good?" — "Fifteen or sixteen," replied the other. — "That's a lot," said Martin.

Candide was very pleased with an actress who played Queen Elizabeth in a fairly dull tragedy which is sometimes performed.[7] "This actress," he said to Martin, "pleases me greatly; she looks rather like Mademoiselle Cunégonde; I would greatly like to pay her my respects." The abbé from Périgord offered to introduce him to her. Candide, raised in Germany, asked what was the etiquette, and how did they treat the queens of England in France. "We must make a distinction," said the abbé. "In the provinces, they take them to a tavern; in Paris, they respect them when they are beautiful, and they throw them in the gutter when they are dead." — "Queens in the gutter!" said Candide. — "Yes, indeed," said Martin, "the abbé is right; I was in Paris when Mademoiselle Monime passed, as they say, from this life to the next; they refused her what these people here call *the honors of burial*, that is to say, of rotting with all the beggars of the neighborhood in a shabby cemetery; she was buried, alone of her troop, at the corner of the Rue de Bourgogne; which must have given her extreme pain, for she was very noble." [8] — "That's very impolite," said Candide. — "What do you expect?" said Martin; "that's how

célèbre actrice (1730). She is remembered here as "Monime" because she made her debut in that role at the Théatre-Français in Racine's *Mithridate*, in 1717.

Martin; ces gens-ci sont ainsi faits. Imaginez toutes les contradictions, toutes les incompatibilités possibles, vous les verrez dans le gouvernement, dans les tribunaux, dans les églises, dans les spectacles de cette drôle de nation. — Est-il vrai qu'on rit toujours à Paris? dit Candide. — Oui, dit l'abbé, mais c'est en enrageant: car on s'y plaint de tout avec de grands éclats de rire; même on y fait en riant les actions les plus détestables."

"Quel est, dit Candide, ce gros cochon qui me disait tant de mal de la pièce où j'ai tant pleuré et des acteurs qui m'ont fait tant de plaisir? — C'est un mal vivant, répondit l'abbé, qui gagne sa vie à dire du mal de toutes les pièces et de tous les livres; il hait quiconque réussit, comme les eunuques haïssent les jouissants; c'est un de ces serpents de la littérature qui se nourrissent de fange et de venin; c'est un folliculaire. — Qu'appelez-vous folliculaire? dit Candide. — C'est, dit l'abbé, un faiseur de feuilles, un Fréron." [9]

C'est ainsi que Candide, Martin et le Périgourdin, raisonnaient sur l'escalier en voyant défiler le monde au sortir de la pièce. "Quoique je sois très empressé de revoir Mademoiselle Cunégonde, dit Candide, je voudrais pourtant souper avec Mademoiselle Clairon, [10] car elle m'a paru admirable."

[9] Elie-Catherine Fréron (1719–76), a competent journalist and lifelong enemy of Voltaire's. The two men disagreed on fundamentals, but their public battles, as they often did in the eighteenth century, descended to personal details. The word "*folliculaire*" with which he characterizes Fréron, seems to be Voltaire's invention.

these people are made. Imagine all contradictions, all possible incompatibilities, you will see them in government, the tribunals, the churches, and the entertainments of this absurd nation." — "Is it true that they are always laughing in Paris?" said Candide. — "Yes," said the abbé, "but while they are furious inside; for here they complain of everything with great shouts of laughter; here they do even the most detestable things while laughing."

"Who is," said Candide, "that fat pig who spoke so ill of the piece at which I cried so much, and of the actors who gave me so much pleasure?" — "He's a living evil," replied the abbé, "who makes his living speaking ill of all the plays and all the books; he hates whoever succeeds, as eunuchs hate revelers; he is one of those serpents of literature who nourish themselves on filth and venom; he's a feuilletonist." — "What do you call a feuilletonist?" said Candide. — "That," said the abbé, "is a scribbler of sheets, a Fréron." [9]

That is how Candide, Martin, and the Périgordian talked on the staircase as they watched everybody file out of the play. "Although I am very eager to see Mademoiselle Cunégonde again," said Candide, "I would still like to have supper with Mademoiselle Clairon,[10] for she seems admirable to me."

[10] Claire-Josèph Lerys, called Mlle Clairon (1723–1803), a leading actress at the Comédie Française who created many roles in Voltaire's tragedies and was Voltaire's close friend for many years.

L'abbé n'était pas homme à approcher de Mademoiselle Clairon, qui ne voyait que bonne compagnie. "Elle est engagée pour ce soir, dit-il; mais j'aurai l'honneur de vous mener chez une dame de qualité et là vous connaîtrez Paris comme si vous y aviez été quatre ans."

Candide, qui était naturellement curieux, se laissa mener chez la dame, au fond du faubourg Saint-Honoré; [11] on y était occupé d'un pharaon; douze tristes pontes [12] tenaient chacun en main un petit livre de cartes, registre cornu de leurs infortunes. Un profond silence régnait, la pâleur était sur le front des pontes, l'inquiétude sur celui du banquier, et la dame du logis, assise auprès de ce banquier impitoyable, remarquait avec des yeux de lynx tous les parolis, tous les sept-et-le-va de campagne, dont chaque joueur cornait ses cartes; elle faisait décorner avec une attention sévère mais polie, et ne se fâchait point, de peur de perdre ses pratiques. La dame se faisait appeler la marquise de Parolignac.[13] Sa fille, âgée de quinze ans, était au nombre des pontes et avertissait d'un clin d'œil des friponneries de ces pauvres gens qui tâchaient de réparer les cruautés du sort. L'abbé périgourdin, Candide, et Martin entrèrent; personne ne se leva, ni les salua, ni les regarda; tous étaient profondément occupés de leurs cartes. "Madame la baronne de Thunder-ten-

[11] This is a wealthy section of the city, inhabited largely by aristocrats.

[12] Gamblers who bet against the bank.

[13] The name is a conflation of *paroli*, meaning double stakes

The abbé was not the man to approach Mademoiselle Clairon, who saw only decent company. "She is busy this evening," he said, "but I shall have the honor of taking you to a lady of quality, and there you will get to know Paris as if you had been here for four years."

Candide, who was naturally curious, let himself be taken to the lady's house, at the far end of the Faubourg Saint-Honoré;[11] there they were occupied with playing faro; twelve sad punters[12] each held a small hand of cards, the extravagant register of their misfortunes. A profound silence reigned, and there was pallor on the punters' foreheads, anxiety on that of the bankers; and the lady of the house, seated next to this pitiless banker, watched with lynx's eyes all the parolis, all the seven-and-go, for which each player turned the corner of his cards upwards; she made them turn them down with a severe but polite look; and did not get angry, for fear of losing her customers. The lady had herself addressed as Marquise de Parolignac.[13] Her daughter, aged fifteen, was among the punters, and indicated with a wink the cheating of these poor people who tried to repair the cruelties of fortune. The abbé from Périgord, Candide, and Martin entered; no one rose, nor greeted them, nor looked at them; all were profoundly occupied with their cards. "Madame

in the card game, and *gnac*, referring to southern France, where this is a common ending for names, and which sent many a poverty-stricken aristocrat to the gambling halls of Paris.

tronckh était plus civile," dit Candide.

Cependant l'abbé s'approcha de l'oreille de la marquise, qui se leva à moitié, honora Candide d'un sourire gracieux, et Martin d'un air de tête tout à fait noble; elle fit donner un siège et un jeu de cartes à Candide, qui perdit cinquante mille francs en deux tailles: après quoi on soupa très gaiement, et tout le monde était étonné que Candide ne fût pas ému de sa perte; les laquais disaient entre eux, dans leur langage de laquais: "Il faut que ce soit quelque milord anglais." [14]

Le souper fut comme la plupart des soupers de Paris: d'abord du silence, ensuite un bruit de paroles qu'on ne distingue point, puis des plaisanteries dont la plupart sont insipides, de fausses nouvelles, de mauvais raisonnements, un peu de politique et beaucoup de médisance; on parla même de livres nouveaux. "Avez-vous vu, dit l'abbé périgourdin, le roman du sieur Gauchat, docteur en théologie? [15] — Oui, répondit un des convives, mais je n'ai pu l'achever. Nous avons une foule d'écrits impertinents, mais tous ensemble n'approchent pas de l'impertinence de Gauchat, docteur en théologie; je suis si rassasié de cette immensité de détestables livres qui nous inondent que je me suis mis à ponter au pharaon. — Et les *Mélanges* de

[14] Another personal reminiscence: in the mid-1740's, Voltaire often accompanied his mistress, Madame du Châtelet, to aristo-cratic gambling places, and more than once thought that she

the Baroness of Thunder-ten-tronckh was more civil," said Candide.

However, the abbé got the Marquise's ear, who half rose, honored Candide with a gracious smile, and Martin with a most noble nod; she had a seat and a hand of cards given to Candide, who lost fifty thousand francs in two deals; after which they had supper very gaily, and everybody was astonished that Candide should not be moved by his loss; the lackeys said to one another in their lackey language: "This must be some English Milord." [14]

The supper was like most suppers in Paris; at first silence, and then a noise of words that could not be distinguished, then jokes, most of them insipid, false news, bad arguments, a little politics, and a great deal of slander; they even talked about new books. "Have you seen," said the abbé from Périgord, "the novel by Sir Gauchat, Doctor of Theology?" [15] "Yes," replied one of the guests; "but I couldn't finish it. We have a mass of insolent writings; but all together don't approach the insolence of Gauchat, Doctor of Theology; I am so fed up with this immensity of detestable books which inundates us that I have taken to punting faro."

was being cheated. English "milords" were proverbial for their wealth and casual irresponsibility.

[15] Gabriel Gauchat (1709–74?), who published a long attack on the *philosophes* in twelve volumes, the *Lettres critiques, ou Réfutation d'écrits modernes contre la religion* (1753–63), in which Voltaire is handled rather severely.

l'archidiacre T . . . ,[16] qu'en dites-vous? dit l'abbé. —
Ah! dit Madame de Parolignac, l'ennuyeux mortel!
comme il vous dit curieusement tout ce que le monde
sait! comme il discute pesamment ce qui ne vaut pas
la peine d'être remarqué légèrement! comme il s'ap-
proprie, sans esprit, l'esprit des autres! comme il gâte ce
qu'il pille! comme il me dégoûte! Mais il ne me dégoû-
tera plus; c'est assez d'avoir lu quelques pages de l'archi-
diacre."

Il y avait à table un homme savant et de goût qui
appuya ce que disait la marquise. On parla ensuite de
tragédies; la dame demanda pourquoi il y avait des
tragédies qu'on jouait quelquefois, et qu'on ne pou-
vait lire. L'homme de goût expliqua très bien comment
une pièce pouvait avoir quelque intérêt et n'avoir
presque aucun mérite; il prouva en peu de mots que
ce n'était pas assez d'amener une ou deux de ces situa-
tions qu'on trouve dans tous les romans, et qui sédui-
sent toujours les spectateurs, mais qu'il faut être neuf
sans être bizarre, souvent sublime et toujours naturel;
connaître le cœur humain et le faire parler; être grand
poète sans que jamais aucun personnage de la pièce
paraisse poète; savoir parfaitement sa langue, la parler
avec pureté, avec une harmonie continue, sans que
jamais la rime coûte rien au sens. "Quiconque, ajou-
ta-t-il, n'observe pas toutes ces règles peut faire une
ou deux tragédies applaudies au théâtre, mais il ne

[16] This initial stands for Nicolas-Charles-Joseph Trublet (1697–
1770), an archdeacon and author of *Essais de littérature et de*

— "And the *Mélanges* of Archdeacon T . . . ,[16] what do you say about them?" said the abbé. — "Ah!" said Madame de Parolignac, "that tedious mortal! How carefully he tells you what everybody knows! How weightily he discusses what isn't worth being noticed lightly! How mindlessly he appropriates the minds of others! How he spoils what he plunders! How he disgusts me! But he won't disgust me any more; it's enough to have read a few pages by the Archdeacon."

There was at the table a man of learning and taste who supported what the Marquise said. Then they talked about tragedies; the lady asked why there were tragedies that were sometimes played, and which one could not read. The man of taste explained very well how a play can have some interest and practically no merit; he proved in a few words that it was not enough to bring in one or two of those situations that are found in all novels, and which always fascinate the spectators, but that one must be novel without being bizarre, often sublime and always natural; know the human heart and make it speak; be a great poet without ever letting any character in the piece appear to be a poet; know one's language perfectly, speak it with purity, with a continuous harmony, without ever making a rhyme at the expense of sense. "Anyone," he added, "who does not observe all of these rules can make one or two tragedies that are applauded in the

morale (1736). He was bitterly hostile to Voltaire, the *Encyclopédie*, and the philosophic movement in general.

sera jamais compté au rang des bons écrivains; il y a très peu de bonnes tragédies: les unes sont des idylles en dialogues bien écrits et bien rimés; les autres, des raisonnements politiques qui endorment, ou des amplifications qui rebutent; les autres, des rêves d'énergumène, en style barbare, des propos interrompus, de longues apostrophes aux dieux, parce qu'on ne sait point parler aux hommes, des maximes fausses, des lieux communs ampoulés." [17]

Candide écouta ce propos avec attention et conçut une grande idée du discoureur; et, comme la marquise avait eu soin de le placer à côté d'elle, il s'approcha de son oreille, et prit la liberté de lui demander qui était cet homme qui parlait si bien. "C'est un savant, dit la dame, qui ne ponte point, et que l'abbé m'amène quelquefois à souper: il se connaît parfaitement en tragédies et en livres, et il a fait une tragédie sifflée et un livre dont on n'a jamais vu hors de la boutique de son libraire qu'un exemplaire qu'il m'a dédié. — Le grand homme! dit Candide; c'est un autre Pangloss."

Alors, se tournant vers lui, il lui dit: "Monsieur, vous pensez sans doute que tout est au mieux dans le monde physique et dans le moral, et que rien ne pouvait être autrement? — Moi, Monsieur, lui répondit le savant, je ne pense rien de tout cela: je trouve que tout va de travers chez nous; que personne ne sait ni

[17] An answer to the criticisms accorded Voltaire's successful tragedy *Tancrède* (1760).

theater, but he will never be counted in the rank of good writers; there are very few good tragedies; some are idylls in well-written and well-rhymed dialogue; the others, political arguments that put one to sleep, or amplifications that repel; the others, enthusiasts' dreams, in barbarous style, in broken speeches, long apostrophes to the gods (because he does not know how to speak to men), false maxims, turgid commonplaces." [17]

Candide listened to the speech with attention, and formed an excellent impression of the speaker; and, since the Marquise had taken care to place him beside her, he got her ear and took the liberty of asking her who that man was who spoke so well. "He's a scholar," said the lady, "who doesn't gamble, and whom the abbé brings here sometimes for supper; he knows his way about perfectly with tragedies and books, and he has written a tragedy that was hissed, and a book of which only one copy, which he dedicated to me, has ever been seen outside his publisher's shop." — "A great man!" said Candide, "he's another Pangloss."

Then, turning towards him, he said to him: "Sir, doubtless you think that all is for the best in the physical and moral world, and that nothing could have been otherwise?" — "I, sir," replied the scholar to him, "I don't think anything of the kind; I find that everything goes wrong with us; that no one knows

quel est son rang, ni quelle est sa charge, ni ce qu'il fait, ni ce qu'il doit faire, et qu'excepté le souper, qui est assez gai et où il paraît assez d'union, tout le reste du temps se passe en querelles impertinentes: jansénistes [18] contre molinistes,[19] gens du parlement contre gens d'église, gens de lettres contre gens de lettres, courtisans contre courtisans, financiers contre le peuple, femmes contre maris, parents contre parents; c'est une guerre éternelle."

Candide lui répliqua: "J'ai vu pis; mais un sage, qui depuis a eu le malheur d'être pendu, m'apprit que tout cela est à merveille: ce sont des ombres à un beau tableau. — Votre pendu se moquait du monde, dit Martin; vos ombres sont des taches horribles. — Ce sont les hommes qui font les taches, dit Candide, et ils ne peuvent pas s'en dispenser. — Ce n'est donc pas leur faute," dit Martin. La plupart des pontes, qui n'entendaient rien à ce langage, buvaient; et Martin raisonna avec le savant, et Candide raconta une partie de ses aventures à la dame du logis.

Après souper, la marquise mena Candide dans son

[18] Followers of Jansenius (1585–1638), Flemish theologian who became bishop of Ypres. In his posthumous *Augustinus* (1640), Jansenius developed severe views on divine grace and argued that few men were elected for salvation. His views were taken up in France by a small group of intellectuals, of whom Blaise Pascal (1623–62), the great mathematician and religious writer, is the most famous. Jansenism was in direct, bitter conflict with the more relaxed theology of the Jesuits, and always in a minority. After alternations of persecution and accommodation, Jansenism was finally condemned by the papal Bull

either what his rank is, nor his job, nor what he is
doing, nor what he should do, and that excepting
supper, which is pretty gay, and where there seems to
be plenty of agreement, all the rest of the time is spent
in nonsensical quarrels; Jansenists [18] against Molinists,[19]
men of Parlement against men of the church, men of
letters against men of letters, courtiers against courtiers,
financiers against the people, wives against husbands,
relatives against relatives; it's an eternal war."

Candide answered him: "I've seen worse; but a sage,
who has since had the misfortune of being hanged,
taught me that all this is wonderful; these are shadows
in a beautiful painting." — "Your hanged man was
making fun of everyone," said Martin; "your shadows
are horrible stains." — "It is men who make the stains,"
said Candide, "and they can't avoid them." — "That's
not their fault," said Martin. Most of the gamblers,
who understood nothing of this sort of conversation,
were drinking; and Martin was having a discussion
with the scholar, and Candide recounted a part of his
adventures to the lady of the house.

After supper, the Marquise took Candide into her

Unigenitus (1713), but Jansenism retained its hold, especially on
the antipapal lower aristocracy, concentrated in the French law
courts, the *parlements*.

[19] Widely used as synonym for Jesuits. The word derives from
the Spanish Jesuit Luis Molina (1535–1600), whose *Concordia*
(1589) tried to reconcile the strength of man's free will with
the supremacy of divine grace. In stressing free will, Molinism
soon came into conflict with the more austere theology of Jan-
senism (*see previous note*).

cabinet et le fit asseoir sur un canapé. "Eh bien! lui dit-elle, vous aimez donc toujours éperdument Mademoiselle Cunégonde de Thunder-ten-tronckh? — Oui, Madame," répondit Candide. La marquise lui répliqua avec un sourire tendre: "Vous me répondez comme un jeune homme de Vestphalie; un Français m'aurait dit: 'Il est vrai que j'ai aimé Mademoiselle Cunégonde; mais, en vous voyant, Madame, je crains de ne la plus aimer.' — Hélas! Madame, dit Candide, je répondrai comme vous voudrez. — Votre passion pour elle, dit la marquise, a commencé en ramassant son mouchoir; je veux que vous ramassiez ma jarretière. — De tout mon cœur," dit Candide; et il la ramassa. "Mais je veux que vous me la remettiez," dit la dame; et Candide la lui remit. "Voyez-vous, dit la dame, vous êtes étranger; je fais quelquefois languir mes amants de Paris quinze jours, mais je me rends à vous dès la première nuit, parce qu'il faut faire les honneurs de son pays à un jeune homme de Vestphalie." La belle, ayant aperçu deux énormes diamants aux deux mains de son jeune étranger, les loua de si bonne foi que des doigts de Candide ils passèrent aux doigts de la marquise.

Candide, en s'en retournant avec son abbé périgourdin, sentit quelques remords d'avoir fait une infidélité à Mademoiselle Cunégonde; monsieur l'abbé entra dans sa peine; il n'avait qu'une légère part aux cinquante mille livres perdues au jeu par Candide, et à la valeur des deux brillants moitié donnés, moitié extorqués. Son dessein était de profiter, autant qu'il le pourrait, des

boudoir and made him sit down on a sofa. "Well!" she said to him, "so you're still madly in love with Mademoiselle Cunégonde of Thunder-ten-tronckh!" — "Yes, Madame," replied Candide. The Marquise answered him with a tender smile: "You answer me like a young man from Westphalia; a Frenchman would have said to me: 'It's true that I once loved Mademoiselle Cunégonde, but, madame, when I see you, I fear I no longer love her.'" — "Alas! Madame," said Candide, "I shall reply as you wish." — "Your passion for her," said the Marquise, "began when you picked up her handkerchief; I want you to pick up my garter." — "With all my heart," said Candide; and he picked it up. "But I want you to put it back on me," said the lady; and Candide put it back on her. "Look," said the lady, "you are a foreigner; sometimes I make my Parisian lovers languish for two weeks, but I surrender to you on the first night, because one must do the honors of one's country to a young man from Westphalia." The beauty, having noticed two enormous diamonds on her young foreigner's two hands, praised them so sincerely that they passed from Candide's fingers to the Marquise's fingers.

Returning home with his Périgordian abbé, Candide felt some remorse at having been unfaithful to Mademoiselle Cunégonde; the abbé took part in his pains; he had had only a small share of the fifty thousand francs that Candide had lost gambling and of the value of the two diamonds half-given, half-extorted. His plan was to profit, as much as he could, from the

avantages que la connaissance de Candide pouvait lui procurer. Il lui parla beaucoup de Cunégonde; et Candide lui dit qu'il demanderait bien pardon à cette belle de son infidélité, quand il la verrait à Venise.

Le Périgourdin redoublait de politesses et d'attentions, et prenait un intérêt tendre à tout ce que Candide disait, à tout ce qu'il faisait, à tout ce qu'il voulait faire.[20] "Vous avez donc, Monsieur, lui dit-il, un rendezvous à Venise? — Oui, Monsieur l'abbé, dit Candide; il faut absolument que j'aille trouver Mademoiselle Cunégonde." Alors, engagé par le plaisir de parler de ce qu'il aimait, il conta, selon son usage, une partie de ses aventures avec cette illustre Vestphalienne.

"Je crois, dit l'abbé, que Mademoiselle Cunégonde a bien de l'esprit, et qu'elle écrit des lettres charmantes. — Je n'en ai jamais reçu, dit Candide: car, figurez-vous qu'ayant été chassé du château pour l'amour d'elle, je ne pus lui écrire; que bientôt après j'appris qu'elle était morte, qu'ensuite je la retrouvai, et que je la perdis, et que je lui ai envoyé à deux mille cinq cents lieues d'ici un exprès dont j'attends la réponse."

L'abbé écoutait attentivement et paraissait un peu rêveur. Il prit bientôt congé des deux étrangers, après les avoir tendrement embrassés. Le lendemain Candide reçut à son réveil une lettre conçue en ces termes:

[20] The passage inserted in 1761 ends here (see note 6 above).

advantages that his acquaintance with Candide could secure for him. He spoke to him a great deal about Cunégonde, and Candide told him that he would certainly ask that beauty's forgiveness for his infidelity when he saw her in Venice.

The Périgordian redoubled his politeness and attentions, and took a tender interest in everything Candide said, everything he did, everything he wanted to do.[20] "Monsieur," he said to him, "you have a rendezvous at Venice then?" — "Yes, Monsieur abbé," said Candide; "I must absolutely go and find Mademoiselle Cunégonde." Then, drawn on by the pleasure of talking about what he loved, he recounted, according to his custom, a part of his adventures with that illustrious lady from Westphalia.

"I believe," said the abbé, "that Mademoiselle Cunégonde has much wit and that she writes charming letters." — "I've never received any from her," said Candide; "for you must recognize that having been thrown out of the country house for love of her, I could not write to her; that soon after I learned that she was dead, then I found her again, and then lost her, and that I have sent her an express dispatch seven thousand five hundred miles from here and am waiting for her reply."

The abbé listened attentively, and seemed in a bit of a reverie. He soon took leave of the two foreigners, after having embraced them tenderly. The next day, when he woke up, Candide received a letter couched in these terms:

215

Monsieur mon très cher amant, il y a huit jours que je suis malade en cette ville; j'apprends que vous y êtes. Je volerais dans vos bras si je pouvais remuer. J'ai su votre passage à Bordeaux; j'y ai laissé le fidèle Cacambo et la vieille, qui doivent bientôt me suivre. Le gouverneur de Buenos-Ayres a tout pris, mais il me reste votre cœur. Venez, votre présence me rendra la vie ou me fera mourir de plaisir.

Cette lettre charmante, cette lettre inespérée, transporta Candide d'une joie inexprimable; et la maladie de sa chère Cunégonde l'accabla de douleur. Partagé entre ces deux sentiments, il prend son or et les diamants, et se fait conduire avec Martin à l'hôtel où Mademoiselle Cunégonde demeurait. Il entre en tremblant d'émotion, son cœur palpite, sa voix sanglote; il veut ouvrir les rideaux du lit, il veut faire apporter de la lumière. "Gardez-vous-en bien, lui dit la suivante, la lumière la tue;" et soudain elle referme le rideau. "Ma chère Cunégonde, dit Candide en pleurant; comment vous portez-vous? si vous ne pouvez me voir, parlez-moi du moins. — Elle ne peut parler," dit la suivante. La dame alors tire du lit une main potelée que Candide arrose longtemps de ses larmes, et qu'il remplit ensuite de diamants, en laissant un sac plein d'or sur le fauteuil.

Au milieu de ses transports arrive un exempt suivi de l'abbé périgourdin et d'une escouade. "Voilà donc, dit-il, ces deux étrangers suspects?" Il les fait incontinent saisir et ordonne à ses braves de les traîner en prison. "Ce n'est pas ainsi qu'on traite les voyageurs dans le Dorado, dit Candide. — Je suis plus manichéen

Monsieur, my dearest lover, I have been sick in this town for a week; I learned that you are here. I would fly to your arms if I could move. I hear that you passed through Bordeaux; I have left the faithful Cacambo and the old woman there, who should soon follow me. The governor of Buenos Aires took everything, but I retain your heart. Come, your presence will restore me to life or make me die of pleasure.

This charming letter, this unexpected letter, enraptured Candide with an inexpressible joy; and the illness of his dear Cunégonde overwhelmed him with grief. Torn between these two feelings, he takes his gold and his diamonds, and has himself taken with Martin to the hotel where Mademoiselle Cunégonde is staying. He enters trembling with emotion, his heart is beating, his voice is sobbing; he wants to open the bed curtains; he wants to have light brought. "Take care you don't," said the waiting maid to him; "light will kill her"; and she quickly closes the curtain again. "My dear Cunégonde," said Candide weeping, "how are you? If you cannot see me, at least speak to me." — "She can't speak," said the waiting maid. The lady then stretches from the bed a plump hand, which Candide bathes with his tears for a long time, and then fills with diamonds, leaving a sack full of gold on the armchair.

In the middle of his raptures a police officer arrives followed by the Périgordian abbé and a squad. "Here, then," he said, "are those two suspicious foreigners." He has them seized immediately and orders his bullies to drag them to prison. "This is not how they treat travelers in El Dorado," said Candide. — "I'm more

que jamais, dit Martin. — Mais, Monsieur, où nous menez-vous? dit Candide. — Dans un cul de basse-fosse," dit l'exempt.

Martin, ayant repris son sang-froid, jugea que la dame qui se prétendait Cunégonde était une friponne, monsieur l'abbé périgourdin un fripon qui avait abusé au plus vite de l'innocence de Candide, et l'exempt un autre fripon dont on pouvait aisément se débarrasser.

Plutôt que de s'exposer aux procédures de la justice, Candide, éclairé par son conseil, et d'ailleurs toujours impatient de revoir la véritable Cunégonde, propose à l'exempt trois petits diamants d'environ trois mille pistoles chacun. "Ah! Monsieur, lui dit l'homme au bâton d'ivoire, eussiez-vous commis tous les crimes imaginables, vous êtes le plus honnête homme du monde. Trois diamants! chacun de trois mille pistoles! Monsieur! je me ferais tuer pour vous, au lieu de vous mener dans un cachot. On arrête tous les étrangers, mais laissez-moi faire; j'ai un frère à Dieppe en Normandie, je vais vous y mener; et si vous avez quelque diamant à lui donner, il aura soin de vous comme moi-même. — Et pourquoi arrête-t-on tous les étrangers?" dit Candide. L'abbé périgourdin prit alors la parole et dit: "C'est parce qu'un gueux du pays d'Atrébatie [21] a entendu dire des sottises: cela seul lui a fait commettre

[21] Latin name for the province of Artois. Here, in the town of Arras, was born Robert-François Damiens (1715–57), who on 5 January 1757 stabbed Louis XV with a dagger, wounding him slightly. Voltaire, who elsewhere describes his cruel execu-

of a Manichean than ever," said Martin. — "But, monsieur, where are you taking us?" said Candide. — "To a deep dungeon," said the police officer.

Martin, having regained his coolness, decided that the lady who claimed to be Cunégonde was a fraud, monsieur the abbé from Périgord a fraud who had taken advantage of Candide's innocence as quickly as possible, and the police officer another fraud whom they could easily get rid of.

Rather than exposing himself to the processes of justice, Candide, enlightened by his advice, and besides still impatient to see the true Cunégonde again, offers the police officer three little diamonds worth about three thousand pistoles each. "Ah! monsieur," says the man with the ivory baton to him, "had you committed all imaginable crimes, you would be the most decent man in the world. Three diamonds! Each worth three thousand pistoles! Monsieur! I would let myself be killed for you, instead of taking you to a dungeon. They arrest all foreigners, but let me manage; I have a brother at Dieppe in Normandy; I'm going to take you there; and if you have some diamonds to give him, he will take care of you as I am doing." — "And why do they arrest all foreigners?" said Candide. The abbé from Périgord then took the floor and said: "It's because a beggar from the land of Atrebatum [21] listened to nonsense; this alone made him commit a parricide,

tion in repulsive detail, blamed this deranged attack on Damiens' religious fanaticism.

un parricide, non pas tel que celui de 1610 au mois de mai, mais tel que celui de 1594 au mois de décembre,[22] et tel que plusieurs autres commis dans d'autres années et dans d'autres mois par d'autres gueux qui avaient entendu dire des sottises."

L'exempt alors expliqua de quoi il s'agissait. "Ah! les monstres! s'écria Candide; quoi! de telles horreurs chez un peuple qui danse et qui chante! Ne pourrai-je sortir au plus vite de ce pays où des singes agacent des tigres? J'ai vu des ours dans mon pays; je n'ai vu des hommes que dans le Dorado. Au nom de Dieu, Monsieur l'exempt, menez-moi à Venise, où je dois attendre Mademoiselle Cunégonde. — Je ne peux vous mener qu'en Basse-Normandie," dit le barigel.[23] Aussitôt il lui fait ôter ses fers, dit qu'il s'est mépris, renvoie ses gens, emmène à Dieppe Candide et Martin, et les laisse entre les mains de son frère. Il y avait un petit vaisseau hollandais à la rade. Le Normand, à l'aide de trois autres diamants devenu le plus serviable des hommes, embarque Candide et ses gens dans le vaisseau qui allait faire voile pour Portsmouth en Angleterre. Ce n'était pas le chemin de Venise; mais Candide croyait être délivré de l'enfer, et il comptait bien reprendre la route de Venise à la première occasion.

[22] The "parricide" of 1594 took place on 27 December 1594; it was the unsuccessful attempt by Jean Chatel (1575–94) to kill Henri IV, Voltaire's favorite French king. The "parricide" of 1610 was the successful assassination, on 14 May, of that king by François Ravaillac (1578–1610). Both men were tortured

not like the one of 1610 in the month of May, but like the one of 1594 in the month of December,[22] and like several others committed in other years in other months by other beggars who had listened to nonsense."

The police officer then explained what it was about. "Ah! the monsters!" Candide exclaimed; "What! Such horrors among a nation that dances and sings! Can't I leave as quickly as possible a country where monkeys stir up tigers? I have seen bears in my country; I have seen men only in El Dorado. In the name of God, monsieur officer, take me to Venice where I am to wait for Mademoiselle Cunégonde." — "I can take you only to Lower Normandy," said the barigel.[23] Immediately he has his chains removed, says that he has been mistaken, sends his men away, and leads Candide and Martin to Dieppe and leaves them in the hands of his brother. There was a small Dutch vessel in the roads. The Norman, who had become the most obliging of men with the help of three other diamonds, embarks Candide and his men in the vessel which is going to set sail for Portsmouth in England. This was not the way to Venice; but Candide thought he was delivered from hell, and fully counted on getting back on the way to Venice at the first opportunity.

and executed, and both, Voltaire thought, had "listened to foolish talk."

[23] An old name for a chief constable in Rome and some other Italian cities.

Chapitre Vingt-troisième

Candide et Martin Vont sur les Côtes d'Angle-
terre; ce Qu'Ils y Voient

"Ah! Pangloss! Pangloss! Ah! Martin! Martin! Ah!
ma chère Cunégonde! qu'est-ce que ce monde-ci?
disait Candide sur le vaisseau hollandais. — Quelque
chose de bien fou et de bien abominable, répondait
Martin. — Vous connaissez l'Angleterre; y est-on aussi
fou qu'en France? — C'est une autre espèce de folie,
dit Martin. Vous savez que ces deux nations sont
en guerre pour quelques arpents de neige vers le
Canada,[1] et qu'elles dépensent pour cette belle guerre
beaucoup plus que tout le Canada ne vaut. De vous
dire précisément s'il y a plus de gens à lier dans un
pays que dans un autre, c'est ce que mes faibles lu-
mières ne me permettent pas; je sais seulement qu'en
général les gens que nous allons voir sont fort atra-
bilaires." [2]

En causant ainsi ils abordèrent à Portsmouth; une
multitude de peuple couvrait le rivage, et regardait
attentivement un assez gros homme qui ètait à genoux,

[1] Voltaire's description of Canada as *quelques arpents de neige*
has often been cited against him, sometimes as a contributing
cause for the French loss of Canada, sometimes as proof of his

Twenty-third Chapter

Candide and Martin Go to the Coast of England; What They See There

"Ah! Pangloss! Pangloss! Ah! Martin! Martin! Ah! my dear Cunégonde! What kind of world is this?" said Candide on the Dutch ship. — "Something very crazy and very abominable," replied Martin. — "You know England; are they as crazy there as in France?" — "That's another kind of madness," said Martin. "You know that these two nations are at war over a few acres of snow around Canada,[1] and that they are spending for that fine war much more than all of Canada is worth. To tell you precisely whether there are more people who need to be tied up in one country than in another, that is something my poor intelligence does not permit me; I only know that in general the people we are going to see are very melancholy."[2]

Talking this way, they arrived at Portsmouth; a crowd of people were covering the shore and looking attentively at a fairly fat man who was on his knees,

obtuseness. The first charge is nonsensical, the second too harsh: it expresses Voltaire's general hatred of war, intensified by the conflict raging at the time he was writing Candide.

[2] The reputation of the English for melancholia was widespread in the eighteenth century.

les yeux bandés, sur le tillac d'un des vaisseaux de la flotte; quatre soldats, postés vis-à-vis de cet homme, lui tirèrent chacun trois balles dans le crâne, le plus paisiblement du monde; et toute l'assemblée s'en retourna extrêmement satisfaite. "Qu'est-ce donc que tout ceci? dit Candide, et quel démon exerce partout son empire?" Il demanda qui était ce gros homme qu'on venait de tuer en cérémonie. "C'est un amiral, lui répondit-on. — Et pourquoi tuer cet amiral? — C'est, lui dit-on, parce qu'il n'a pas fait tuer assez de monde; il a livré un combat à un amiral français, et on a trouvé qu'il n'était pas assez près delui. — Mais, dit Candide, l'amiral français était aussi loin de l'amiral anglais que celui-ci l'était de l'autre! — Cela est incontestable, lui répliqua-t-on; mais dans ce pays-ci il est bon de tuer de temps en temps un amiral pour encourager les autres." [3]

Candide fut si étourdi et si choqué de ce qu'il voyait et de ce qu'il entendait qu'il ne voulut pas seulement mettre pied à terre, et qu'il fit son marché avec le patron hollandais (dût-il le voler comme celui de Surinam) pour le conduire sans délai à Venise.

Le patron fut prêt au bout de deux jours. On côtoya la France; on passa à la vue de Lisbonne, et Candide frémit. On entra dans le détroit et dans la Méditerranée; enfin on aborda à Venise. "Dieu soit loué! dit Candide en embrassant Martin; c'est ici que je reverrai la belle Cunégonde. Je compte sur Cacambo comme sur moi-même. Tout est bien, tout va bien, tout va le mieux qu'il soit possible."

[3] See Introduction, p. x.

his eyes bandaged, on the main deck of one of the vessels of the fleet; four soldiers, posted face to face with this man, each put three bullets into his skull, as peacefully as possible; and the whole assembly went back home extremely satisfied. "Well, what is all this?" said Candide; "and what demon exercises his power everywhere?" He asked who was that fat man who had just been killed so ceremoniously. "He was an admiral," he was told. — "And why kill this admiral?" — "That's because," he was told, "he did not get enough people killed; he gave battle to a French admiral, and it was decided that he was not close enough to him." — "But," said Candide, "the French admiral was as far from the English admiral as the latter was from the former!" — "That is undeniable," they told him; "but in this country it is good to kill an admiral from time to time to encourage the others." [3]

Candide was so stunned and so shocked by what he had seen and heard that he did not even want to set foot on land, and made his bargain with the Dutch captain (should he rob him like the one of Surinam) to take him to Venice without delay.

The captain was ready at the end of two days. They sailed along the coast of France; they passed in sight of Lisbon, and Candide shuddered. They entered through the Straits and into the Mediterranean; finally they landed in Venice. "God be praised!" said Candide, embracing Martin, "here is where I shall see the beautiful Cunégonde again. I'm counting on Cacambo as on myself. All is well, all goes well, all goes as well as it possibly could."

Chapitre Vingt-quatrième

De Paquette, et de Frère Giroflée

Dès qu'il fut à Venise, il fit chercher Cacambo dans tous les cabarets, dans tous les cafés, chez toutes les filles de joie, et ne le trouva point. Il envoyait tous les jours à la découverte de tous les vaisseaux et de toutes les barques: nulles nouvelles de Cacambo. "Quoi! disait-il à Martin, j'ai eu le temps de passer de Surinam à Bordeaux, d'aller de Bordeaux à Paris, de Paris à Dieppe, de Dieppe à Portsmouth, de côtoyer le Portugal et l'Espagne, de traverser toute la Méditerranée, de passer quelques mois à Venise, et la belle Cunégonde n'est point venue! Je n'ai rencontré au lieu d'elle qu'une drôlesse et un abbé périgourdin! Cunégonde est morte sans doute; je n'ai plus qu'à mourir. Ah! il valait mieux rester dans le paradis du Dorado que de revenir dans cette maudite Europe. Que vous avez raison, mon cher Martin! tout n'est qu'illusion et calamité."

Il tomba dans une mélancolie noire, et ne prit aucune part à l'opéra *alla moda* ni aux autres divertissements du carnaval; pas une dame ne lui donna la moindre tentation. Martin lui dit: "Vous êtes bien simple, en

Twenty-fourth Chapter

Paquette and Friar Giroflée

As soon as he was in Venice, he searched for Cacambo in all the inns and all the cafés, among all the ladies of pleasure, and did not find him. Every day he sent to investigate all the vessels and all the boats; no news of Cacambo. "What!" he said to Martin, "I have had time to cross from Surinam to Bordeaux, go from Bordeaux to Paris, from Paris to Dieppe, from Dieppe to Portsmouth, to sail along the coasts of Portugal and Spain, cross the whole Mediterranean, spend several months in Venice, and the beautiful Cunégonde has not come! In her place I have met only a hussy and an abbé from Périgord! Cunégonde is dead, beyond doubt; there is nothing left for me but die. Ah! It would have been better to stay in the paradise of El Dorado than to return to this cursed Europe. How right you are, my dear Martin! All is but illusion and calamity."

He fell into a black melancholy, and took no part in the opera à la mode, nor other diversions of the carnival; not one lady caused him the slightest temptation. Martin said to him: "You are really very simple,

vérité, de vous figurer qu'un valet métis qui a cinq ou six millions dans ses poches ira chercher votre maîtresse au bout du monde et vous l'amènera à Venise. Il la prendra pour lui, s'il la trouve; s'il ne la trouve pas, il en prendra une autre: je vous conseille d'oublier votre valet Cacambo et votre maîtresse Cunégonde." Martin n'était pas consolant. La mélancolie de Candide augmenta, et Martin ne cessait de lui prouver qu'il y avait peu de vertu et peu de bonheur sur la terre, excepté peut-être dans Eldorado, où personne ne pouvait aller.

En disputant sur cette matière importante, et en attendant Cunégonde, Candide aperçut un jeune théatin [1] dans la place Saint-Marc, qui tenait sous le bras une fille. Le théatin paraissait frais, potelé, vigoureux; ses yeux étaient brillants, son air assuré, sa mine haute, sa démarche fière. La fille était très jolie, et chantait; elle regardait amoureusement son théatin, et de temps en temps lui pinçait ses grosses joues. "Vous m'avouerez du moins, dit Candide à Martin, que ces gens-ci sont heureux. Je n'ai trouvé jusqu'à présent dans toute la terre habitable, excepté dans Eldorado, que des infortunés; mais, pour cette fille et ce théatin, je gage que ce sont des créatures très heureuses. — Je gage que non, dit Martin. — Il n'y a qu'à les prier à dîner, dit Candide, et vous verrez si je me trompe."

Aussitôt il les aborde, il leur fait son compliment, et les invite à venir à son hôtellerie manger des maca-

[1] Member of a regular order founded in 1524 to reform the Catholic clergy from within. One of its founders was J. P.

to imagine that a half-breed valet who has five or six millions in his pockets will look for your mistress at the end of the world and bring her to you in Venice. He will take her for himself if he finds her. If he doesn't find her, he'll take another one; I advise you to forget your valet Cacambo and your mistress Cunégonde." Martin was not consoling. Candide's melancholy grew, and Martin never ceased proving to him that there was little virtue and little happiness on earth; except perhaps in El Dorado, to which no one could go.

While arguing about this important matter and while waiting for Cunégonde, Candide not ced a young Theatine [1] in the Piazza San Marco, a girl under his arm. The Theatine appeared fresh, plump, vigorous; his eyes were brilliant, his manner assured, his head erect, his bearing proud. The girl was very pretty, and was singing; she looked at her Theatine amorously, and from time to time pinched his fat cheeks. "At least you will admit to me," said Candide to Martin, "that these people here are happy. Up to now I have found in all the habitable earth, except in El Dorado, none but unfortunates; but as for this girl and this Theatine, I bet that they are very happy creatures." — "I bet not," said Martin. — "We have only to ask them to dinner," said Candide, "and you will see if I'm wrong."

He accosts them immediately, he pays his respects to them, and invites them to come to his hostelry and

Caraffa, bishop of Chieti (which is Theato in Latin)—hence the name.

ronis, des perdrix de Lombardie, des œufs d'esturgeon, et à boire du vin de Montepulciano, du lacryma-christi, du chypre, et du samos. La demoiselle rougit, le théatin accepta la partie, et la fille le suivit en regardant Candide avec des yeux de surprise et de confusion qui furent obscurcis de quelques larmes. A peine fut-elle entrée dans la chambre de Candide qu'elle lui dit: "Eh quoi! Monsieur Candide ne reconnaît plus Paquette!" A ces mots, Candide, qui ne l'avait pas considérée jusque-là avec attention, parce qu'il n'était occupé que de Cunégonde, lui dit: "Hélas! ma pauvre enfant, c'est donc vous qui avez mis le docteur Pangloss dans le bel état où je l'ai vu? — Hélas! Monsieur, c'est moi-même, dit Paquette; je vois que vous êtes instruit de tout. J'ai su les malheurs épouvantables arrivés à toute la maison de madame la baronne et à la belle Cunégonde. Je vous jure que ma destinée n'a guère été moins triste. J'étais fort innocente quand vous m'avez vue. Un cordelier qui était mon confesseur me séduisit aisément. Les suites en furent affreuses; je fus obligée de sortir du château quelque temps après que monsieur le baron vous eut renvoyé à grands coups de pied dans le derrière. Si un fameux médecin n'avait pas pris pitié de moi, j'étais morte. Je fus quelque temps par reconnaissance la maîtresse de ce médecin. Sa femme, qui était jalouse à la rage, me battait tous les jours impitoyablement; c'était une furie. Ce médecin était le plus laid de tous les hommes, et moi la plus malheureuse de toutes les créatures d'être battue continuellement pour un homme que je n'aimais pas. Vous savez, Monsieur, combien il est dangereux pour une femme acariâtre d'être l'épouse d'un médecin. Celui-ci, outré des pro-

eat macaroni, Lombardy partridges, caviar, and drink Montepulciano, Lacrima Christi, Cyprus, and Samos wine. The young lady blushes, the Theatine accepts the invitation, and the girl follows him looking at Candide with eyes of surprise and confusion, which are dimmed with a few tears. Hardly has she entered Candide's room when she says to him: "Well! Monsieur Candide no longer recognizes Paquette!" At these words, Candide, who had not looked at her attentively until then, because he was occupied with Cunégonde alone, says to her: "Alas! my poor child, so it was you who put Doctor Pangloss in the fine condition I saw him in?" — "Alas! monsieur, I myself," says Paquette; "I see that you are informed about everything. I learned about the horrible misfortunes that happened to the whole house of Madame the Baroness and the beautiful Cunégonde. I swear to you that my destiny has hardly been less sad. I was extremely innocent when you knew me. A Franciscan who was my confessor easily seduced me. The consequences were horrible; I was obliged to leave the country house sometime after Monsieur the Baron had sent you off with great kicks in the behind. If a famous physician had not taken pity on me I would have died. Out of gratitude I was this physician's mistress for some time. His wife, who was jealous to insanity, beat me pitilessly every day; she was a fury. This physician was the ugliest of all men, and I the most unhappy of all creatures to be beaten continually for a man whom I did not love. You know, monsieur, how dangerous it is for a quarrelsome woman to be a physician's wife. This man, outraged by his wife's behavior, gave her one day, to

231

cédés de sa femme, lui donna un jour, pour la guérir d'un petit rhume, une médecine si efficace qu'elle en mourut en deux heures de temps dans des convulsions horribles. Les parents de madame intentèrent à monsieur un procès criminel; il prit la fuite, et moi je fus mise en prison. Mon innocence ne m'aurait pas sauvée si je n'avais été un peu jolie. Le juge m'élargit à condition qu'il succéderait au médecin. Je fus bientôt supplantée par une rivale, chassée sans récompense, et obligée de continuer ce métier abominable qui vous paraît si plaisant à vous autres hommes, et qui n'est pour nous qu'un abîme de misères. J'allai exercer la profession à Venise. Ah! Monsieur, si vous pouviez vous imaginer ce que c'est que d'être obligée de caresser indifféremment un vieux marchand, un avocat, un moine, un gondolier, un abbé; d'être exposée à toutes les insultes, à toutes les avanies; d'être souvent réduite à emprunter une jupe pour aller se la faire lever par un homme dégoûtant; d'être volée par l'un de ce qu'on a gagné avec l'autre; d'être rançonnée par les officiers de justice, et de n'avoir en perspective qu'une vieillesse affreuse, un hôpital et un fumier, vous concluriez que je suis une des plus malheureuses créatures du monde."

Paquette ouvrait ainsi son cœur au bon Candide, dans un cabinet, en présence de Martin, qui disait à Candide: "Vous voyez que j'ai déjà gagné la moitié de la gageure."

Frère Giroflée était resté dans la salle à manger, et buvait un coup en attendant le dîner. "Mais, dit Candide à Paquette, vous aviez l'air si gai, si content, quand je vous ai rencontrée; vous chantiez, vous caressiez le théatin avec une complaisance naturelle; vous m'avez

cure her of a little cold, a medicine so effective that she died of it in two hours' time in horrible convulsions. Madame's relatives brought a criminal prosecution against monsieur; he took flight, and I, I was put into prison. My innocence would not have saved me if I had not been a little pretty. The judge set me free on condition that he succeed the physician. I was soon supplanted by a rival, thrown out without compensation, and obliged to continue this abominable trade which seems so pleasant to you men, and which is nothing but an abyss of misery for us. I went to practice the profession in Venice. Ah! monsieur, if you could imagine what it is to be obliged to caress indiscriminately an old merchant, a lawyer, a monk, a gondolier, an abbé; to be exposed to every insult, to every affront; often to be reduced to borrowing a skirt to go have it lifted by a disgusting man; to be robbed by one of what you have earned with another; to pay extortion money to officers of the law, and to have in prospect nothing but a frightful old age, a poor house, and a dunghill: you would conclude that I am one of the most miserable creatures in the world."

Thus Paquette opened her heart to good Candide in the private room in the presence of Martin, who said to Candide: "You see, I have already won half of the bet."

Friar Giroflée had stayed in the dining room and was having a glass while waiting for dinner. "But," said Candide to Paquette, "you looked so gay, so content, when I met you; you were singing, you were caressing the Theatine with a natural complaisance; you seemed

233

paru aussi heureuse que vous prétendez être infortunée.
— Ah! Monsieur, répondit Paquette, c'est encore là
une des misères du métier. J'ai été hier volée et battue
par un officier, et il faut aujourd'hui que je paraisse de
bonne humeur pour plaire à un moine."

Candide n'en voulut pas davantage; il avoua que
Martin avait raison. On se mit à table avec Paquette
et le théatin; le repas fut assez amusant, et sur la fin
on se parla avec quelque confiance. "Mon père, dit
Candide au moine, vous me paraissez jouir d'une desti-
née que tout le monde doit envier; la fleur de la santé
brille sur votre visage, votre physionomie annonce le
bonheur; vous avez une très jolie fille pour votre
récréation, et vous paraissez très content de votre état
de théatin.

"Ma foi, Monsieur, dit frère Giroflée, je voudrais
que tous les théatins fussent au fond de la mer. J'ai
été tenté cent fois de mettre le feu au couvent, et
d'aller me faire Turc. Mes parents me forcèrent à l'âge
de quinze ans d'endosser cette détestable robe, pour
laisser plus de fortune à un maudit frère aîné, que Dieu
confonde! La jalousie, la discorde, la rage, habitent
dans le couvent. Il est vrai que j'ai prêché quelques
mauvais sermons qui m'ont valu un peu d'argent dont
le prieur me vole la moitié: le reste me sert à entretenir
des filles; mais, quand je rentre le soir dans le monastère,
je suis prêt de me casser la tête contre les murs du
dortoir; et tous mes confrères sont dans le même cas." [2]

[2] This is, of course, a characteristic sally; one may find similar
charges against the monastic life not only throughout all of

as happy to me as you claim to be unfortunate." — "Ah! monsieur," replied Paquette, "that is yet another of the miseries of the trade. Yesterday I was robbed and beaten by an officer, and today I must appear to be in a good mood to please a monk."

Candide wanted no more; he admitted that Martin was right. They sat down to table with Paquette and the Theatine; the meal was fairly entertaining, and at the end they talked to one another with some candor. "Father," said Candide to the monk, "you seem to me to be enjoying the destiny that everyone should envy; the flower of health shines on your face, your physiognomy expresses happiness; you have a very pretty girl for your recreation, and you seem very content with your condition as a Theatine."

"Upon my faith, monsieur," said Friar Giroflée, "I wish all Theatines were at the bottom of the sea. I have been tempted many times to set fire to the monastery, and go turn Turk. My parents forced me, at the age of fifteen, to put on this detestable robe in order to leave a larger portion to a cursed older brother whom God confound! Jealousy, discord, fury inhabit the monastery. It is true that I have preached a few bad sermons which have brought me a little money, half of which the prior steals from me; the rest serves me to keep girls; but when I return to the monastery in the evening I am ready to break my head against the wall of the dormitory; and all my confrères are in the same situation." [2]

Voltaire's writings, but the literature of the Enlightenment in general.

Martin se tournant vers Candide avec son sang-froid ordinaire: "Eh bien! lui dit-il, n'ai-je pas gagné la gageure tout entière?" Candide donna deux mille piastres à Paquette et mille piastres à frère Giroflée. "Je vous réponds, dit-il, qu'avec cela ils seront heureux. — Je n'en crois rien du tout, dit Martin; vous les rendrez peut-être avec ces piastres beaucoup plus malheureux encore. — Il en sera ce qui pourra, dit Candide; mais une chose me console, je vois qu'on retrouve souvent les gens qu'on ne croyait jamais retrouver; il se pourra bien faire qu'ayant rencontré mon mouton rouge et Paquette, je rencontre aussi Cunégonde. — Je souhaite, dit Martin, qu'elle fasse un jour votre bonheur; mais c'est de quoi je doute fort. — Vous êtes bien dur, dit Candide. — C'est que j'ai vécu, dit Martin. — Mais regardez ces gondoliers, dit Candide; ne chantent-ils pas sans cesse? — Vous ne les voyez pas dans leur ménage, avec leurs femmes et leurs marmots d'enfants, dit Martin. Le doge a ses chagrins, les gondoliers ont les leurs. Il est vrai qu'à tout prendre le sort d'un gondolier est préférable à celui d'un doge; mais je crois la différence si médiocre que cela ne vaut pas la peine d'être examiné."

"On parle, dit Candide, du sénateur Pococuranté [3] qui demeure dans ce beau palais sur la Brenta, et qui reçoit assez bien les étrangers. On prétend que c'est un homme qui n'a jamais eu de chagrin. — Je voudrais voir une espèce si rare," dit Martin. Candide aussitôt fit demander au seigneur Pococuranté la permission de venir le voir le lendemain.

[3] Derived from the Italian, meaning "caring little."

Martin, turning towards Candide with his customary coolness, said to him: "Well! Haven't I won the whole bet?" Candide gave two thousand piastres to Paquette and a thousand piastres to Friar Giroflée. "I'll guarantee you," he said, "that with this they will be happy." — "I believe nothing of the sort," said Martin, "with these piastres you will perhaps make them much more unhappy still." — "That may be," said Candide; "but one thing consoles me, I see that we often find the people again whom we thought we would never find again; it may well be that having encountered my red sheep and Paquette, I shall also encounter Cunégonde." — "I hope," said Martin, "that one day she'll make your happiness; but that is something I strongly doubt." — "You are very harsh," said Candide. — "That's because I have lived," said Martin. — "But look at these gondoliers," said Candide; "don't they sing all the time?" — "You don't see them in their household with their wives and their bratty children," said Martin. "The Doge has his troubles, the gondoliers have theirs. It's true, taking it all in all, the lot of a gondolier is preferable to that of a Doge; but I think the difference so slight that it is not worth examining."

"They speak," said Candide, "of Senator Pococuranté,[3] who lives in the handsome palace on the Brenta, and who welcomes foreigners quite decently. They claim he is a man who has never known grief." — "I'd like to see so rare a species," said Martin. Right away Candide sent to ask Lord Pococuranté for permission to come to see him the next day.

Chapitre Vingt-cinquième

Visite Chez le Seigneur Pococuranté, Noble Vénitien

Candide et Martin allèrent en gondole sur la Brenta et arrivèrent au palais du noble Pococuranté. Les jardins étaient bien entendus et ornés de belles statues de marbre; le palais, d'une belle architecture. Le maître du logis, homme de soixante ans, fort riche, reçut très poliment les deux curieux, mais avec très peu d'empressement, ce qui déconcerta Candide et ne déplut point à Martin.

D'abord deux filles jolies et proprement mises servirent du chocolat qu'elles firent très bien mousser. Candide ne put s'empêcher de les louer sur leur beauté, sur leur bonne grâce, et sur leur adresse. "Ce sont d'assez bonnes créatures, dit le sénateur Pococuranté; je les fais quelquefois coucher dans mon lit, car je suis bien las des dames de la ville, de leurs coquetteries, de leurs jalousies, de leurs querelles, de leurs humeurs, de leurs petitesses, de leur orgueil, de leurs sottises, et des sonnets qu'il faut faire ou commander pour elles; mais, après tout, ces deux filles commencent fort à m'ennuyer."

Twenty-fifth Chapter

Visit with Lord Pococuranté, Venetian Noble-man

Candide and Martin went to the Brenta in a gondola, and arrived at the palace of the noble Pococuranté. The gardens were well conceived, and ornamented with handsome marble statues; the palace was of a handsome architecture. The master of the house, a man of sixty, very rich, received the two curious visitors very politely but with very little cordiality, which disconcerted Candide and did not displease Martin.

First two pretty and neatly dressed girls served chocolate, which they had made very fluffy. Candide could not refrain from praising them for their beauty, their grace, and their dexterity. "They are pretty good creatures," said Senator Pococuranté; "I sometimes make them sleep in my bed; for I am very tired of the ladies of the town, of their coquetries, their jealousies, their quarrels, their moods, their pettinesses, their pride, their follies, and the sonnets one must write or order for them; but, after all these two girls are beginning to bore me greatly."

Candide, après le déjeuner, se promenant dans une longue galerie, fut surpris de la beauté des tableaux. Il demanda de quel maître étaient les deux premiers. "Ils sont de Raphaël, dit le sénateur; je les achetai fort cher par vanité il y a quelques années; on dit que c'est ce qu'il y a de plus beau en Italie, mais ils ne me plaisent point du tout: la couleur en est très rembrunie, les figures ne sont pas assez arrondies, et ne sortent point assez; les draperies ne ressemblent en rien à une étoffe: en un mot, quoi qu'on en dise, je ne trouve point là une imitation vraie de la nature. Je n'aimerai un tableau que quand je croirai voir la nature elle-même: il n'y a en point de cette espèce. J'ai beaucoup de tableaux, mais je ne les regarde plus."

Pococuranté, en attendant le dîner, se fit donner un concerto. Candide trouva la musique délicieuse. "Ce bruit, dit Pococuranté, peut amuser une demi-heure; mais, s'il dure plus longtemps, il fatigue tout le monde, quoique personne n'ose l'avouer. La musique aujourd'hui n'est plus que l'art d'exécuter des choses difficiles, et ce qui n'est que difficile ne plaît point à la longue.

"J'aimerais peut-être mieux l'opéra, si on n'avait pas trouvé le secret d'en faire un monstre qui me révolte. Ira voir qui voudra de mauvaises tragédies en musique, où les scènes ne sont faites que pour amener très mal à propos deux ou trois chansons ridicules qui font valoir le gosier d'une actrice; se pâmera de plaisir qui voudra ou qui pourra, en voyant un châtré fredonner le rôle de César et de Caton, et se promener d'un air

Candide, walking in a long gallery after breakfast, was astonished at the beauty of the pictures. He asked what master had painted the first two. "They are by Raphael," said the Senator; "I bought them very expensively out of vanity a few years ago; they are supposed to be the most beautiful things in Italy, but they don't please me at all; their color has turned very dark brown, the figures are not rounded enough and do not stand out enough; the draperies don't resemble cloth at all; in a word, whatever they say, I don't find in them a true imitation of nature. I will only like a picture when I think I am seeing nature itself; there aren't any of that kind. I have many pictures, but I no longer look at them."

Pococuranté, while waiting for dinner, had a concerto played for him. Candide found the music delightful. "This noise," said Pococuranté, "may be entertaining for half an hour; but if it lasts longer, it wearies everybody, although nobody dares admit it. Music today is nothing more than the art of executing difficult things, and in the long run that which is nothing but difficult does not please.

"Perhaps I would like the opera better, if they hadn't found the secret of making it a monster that revolts me. Let those that want go to see bad tragedies set to music, where the scenes are composed only to bring in two or three ridiculous songs very maladroitly to show off an actress's voice; let those who want, or who can, faint with pleasure at seeing a castrato trill the role of Caesar and Cato, and tread the boards with an awk-

gauche sur des planches; pour moi, il y a longtemps que j'ai renoncé à ces pauvretés, qui font aujourd'hui la gloire de l'Italie, et que des souverains payent si chèrement." Candide disputa un peu, mais avec discrétion.[1] Martin fut entièrement de l'avis du sénateur.

On se mit à table; et, après un excellent dîner, on entra dans la bibliothèque. Candide, en voyant un Homère magnifiquement relié, loua l'illustrissime sur son bon goût. "Voilà, dit-il, un livre qui faisait les délices du grand Pangloss, le meilleur philosophe de l'Allemagne. — Il ne fait pas les miennes, dit froidement Pococuranté; on me fit accroire autrefois que j'avais du plaisir en le lisant; mais cette répétition continuelle de combats qui se ressemblent tous, ces dieux qui agissent toujours pour ne rien faire de décisif, cette Hélène qui est le sujet de la guerre, et qui à peine est une actrice de la pièce; cette Troie qu'on assiège et qu'on ne prend point, tout cela me causait le plus mortel ennui. J'ai demandé quelquefois à des savants s'ils s'ennuyaient autant que moi à cette lecture: tous les gens sincères m'ont avoué que le livre leur tombait des mains, mais qu'il fallait toujours l'avoir dans sa bibliothèque, comme un monument de l'antiquité, et comme ces médailles rouillées qui ne peuvent être de commerce."

[1] This sentence, like the statement on p. 251 that Candide liked Homer and respected Milton, should be taken as a clue: the sweeping disdain of Pococuranté for these masters of Western literature does not represent the whole of Voltaire's views.

ward air; as for me, I have long given up these sorts of things which today are the glory of Italy, and which sovereigns pay so much for." Candide argued a little, but with discretion.[1] Martin was entirely of the Senator's opinion.

They sat down to table; and after an excellent dinner they went into the library. Candide, seeing a magnificently bound Homer, praised the Illustrissimo for his good taste. "Here's a book," he said, "that was the delight of the great Pangloss, the best philosopher of Germany." — "It isn't mine," said Pococuranté coldly; "at one time I was made to believe that I had pleasure in reading it; but that continual repetition of combats which all resemble one another, those gods who always act in order to do nothing decisive, that Helen who is the subject of the war and who hardly has a part in the play; that Troy which is besieged and not taken; all that has caused me the most deadly boredom. I have sometimes asked scholars if they were as bored as I was in reading it; all the sincere men have admitted to me that the book fell from their hands, but that one must always have it in one's library, as a monument of antiquity, or like those rusty coins which cannot be put into circulation."

Voltaire prided himself on his intellectual independence, on knowing what he liked, and the criticisms expressed on this and the following pages can for the most part be found in his early *Essai sur la poésie épique* (1728). But Voltaire is not Pococuranté, for Voltaire knew how to admire, too.

"Votre Excellence ne pense pas ainsi de Virgile? dit Candide. — Je conviens, dit Pococuranté, que le second, le quatrième, et le sixième livre de son *Énéide* sont excellents; mais pour son pieux Énée, et le fort Cloanthe, et l'ami Achates, et le petit Ascanius, et l'imbécile roi Latinus, et la bourgeoise Amata, et l'insipide Lavinia, je ne crois pas qu'il y ait rien de si froid et de plus désagréable. J'aime mieux le Tasse et les contes à dormir debout de l'Arioste."

"Oserais-je vous demander, Monsieur, dit Candide, si vous n'avez pas un grand plaisir à lire Horace? — Il y a des maximes, dit Pococuranté, dont un homme du monde peut faire son profit, et qui, étant resserrées dans des vers énergiques, se gravent plus aisément dans la mémoire; mais je me soucie fort peu de son voyage à Brindes,[2] et de sa description d'un mauvais dîner,[3] et de la querelle de crocheteurs entre je ne sais quel Pupilus,[4] dont les paroles, dit-il, *étaient pleines de pus,* et un autre dont les paroles *étaient du vinaigre.*[5] Je n'ai lu qu'avec un extrême dégoût ses vers grossiers contre des vieilles et contre des sorcières;[6] et je ne vois pas quel mérite il peut y avoir à dire à son ami Mæcenas que, s'il est mis par lui au rang des poètes lyriques, il frappera les astres de son front sublime.[7] Les sots admirent tout dans un auteur estimé. Je ne lis que

[2] See Horace, *Satires,* I, v. While Voltaire liked Horace and often quotes him, the merit of this particular work eluded him.

[3] *Satires,* II, viii.

[4] *Satires,* I, vii. The name should be Rupilius.

[5] This is not quite accurate, as a reading of *Satires,* I, vii, will

"Your Excellency doesn't think that way about Virgil?" said Candide. — "I admit," said Pococuranté, "that the second, the fourth, and the sixth books of his *Aeneid* are excellent; but as for his pious Aeneas and the strong Cloanthes, and the faithful Achates, and the little Ascanius, and the imbecilic King Latinus, and the bourgeois Amata, and the insipid Lavinia, I don't believe that there is anything so cold and disagreeable. I prefer Tasso and the fantastic tales of Ariosto."

"May I venture to ask you, monsieur," said Candide, "if reading Horace doesn't give you great pleasure?" — "There are maxims," said Pococuranté, "from which a man of the world can draw profit, and which, being compressed in energetic verses, engrave themselves more easily on the memory; but I care very little about his trip to Brindisi,[2] and his description of a bad dinner,[3] and the blackguards' quarrel between someone named Pupilus,[4] whose words, he said, *were full of pus*, and someone else whose words *were of vinegar*.[5] I have read his coarse verses against old women and against witches with extreme disgust;[6] and I don't see what merit there can be in telling his friend Maecenas that, if he is placed by him in the rank of lyric poets, he will strike the stars with his lofty forehead.[7] Fools admire everything in a highly esteemed author. I read for myself

show. One point here is eighteenth-century fastidiousness, which, still basing itself on neoclassical canons of taste, disliked such coarse words as "pus."

[6] See *Epodes*, v, viii, xii.

[7] *Odes*, i, i.

pour moi; je n'aime que ce qui est à mon usage."
Candide, qui avait été élevé à ne jamais juger de rien
par lui-même, était fort étonné de ce qu'il entendait;
et Martin trouvait le façon de penser de Pococuranté
assez raisonnable.

"Oh! voici un Cicéron, dit Candide; pour ce grand
homme-là, je pense que vous ne vous lassez point de
le lire? — Je ne le lis jamais, répondit le Vénitien.
Que m'importe qu'il ait plaidé pour Rabirius ou pour
Cluentius? J'ai bien assez des procès que je juge; je
me serais mieux accommodé de ses œuvres philoso-
phiques; mais, quand j'ai vu qu'il doutait de tout, j'ai
conclu que j'en savais autant que lui et que je n'avais
besoin de personne pour être ignorant." [8]

"Ah! voilà quatre-vingts volumes de recueils d'une
académie des sciences, s'écria Martin; il se peut qu'il y
ait là du bon. — Il y en aurait, dit Pococuranté, si un
seul des auteurs de ces fatras avait inventé seulement
l'art de faire des épingles; mais il n'y a dans tous ces
livres que de vains systèmes et pas une seule chose
utile."

"Que de pièces de théâtre je vois là, dit Candide,
en italien, en espagnol, en français! — Oui, dit le séna-
teur, il y en a trois mille, et pas trois douzaines de
bonnes. Pour ces recueils de sermons, qui tous en-
semble ne valent pas une page de Sénèque,[9] et tous

[8] This passage alone shows Voltaire's distance from Pococu-
ranté: Cicero was his favorite among the ancients—he wrote a
play about him to acquaint the younger generation with his
merits (*Rome sauvée*), quoted him incessantly, and called his
De Divinatione and *De Officiis* the best books of antiquity.

alone; I like only what I can use." Candide, who had been raised never to judge anything for himself, was greatly astonished at what he heard; and Martin found Pococuranté's way of thinking quite reasonable.

"Oh! Here's a Cicero," said Candide; "when it comes to that great man, I suppose that you don't get tired of reading him?" — "I never read him," replied the Venetian. "What does it matter to me whether he pleaded for Rabirius or for Cluentius? I have quite enough with the cases I judge; I would have reconciled myself better to his philosophical works; but when I saw that he doubted everything, I concluded that I knew as much about it as he did, and that I needed no help from anyone to be ignorant." [8]

"Ah! Here are eighty volumes of proceedings of an Academy of Sciences," exclaimed Martin; "there may be something good in those." — "There would be," said Pococuranté, "if a single one of the authors of this trash had merely invented the art of making pins; but in all those books there is nothing but empty systems and not a single useful thing."

"What a lot of plays I see there," said Candide, "in Italian, in Spanish, in French!" — "Yes," said the Senator, "there are three thousand of them and not three dozen good ones. As for these collections of sermons, which all together aren't worth one page of Seneca,[9] and all those fat volumes of theology, you can well

───────────

[9] Here Pococuranté does sound like Voltaire: the practical philosophy of the ancients, with its emphasis on ethics, struck Voltaire as the right employment of man's reason.

ces gros volumes de théologie, vous pensez que je ne les ouvre jamais, ni moi ni personne."

Martin aperçut des rayons chargés de livres anglais. "Je crois, dit-il, qu'un républicain doit se plaire à la plupart de ces ouvrages écrits si librement. — Oui, répondit Pococuranté, il est beau d'écrire ce qu'on pense; c'est le privilège de l'homme. Dans toute notre Italie, on n'écrit que ce qu'on ne pense pas; ceux qui habitent la patrie des Césars et des Antonins n'osent avoir une idée sans la permission d'un jacobin.[10] Je serais content de la liberté qui inspire les génies anglais si la passion et l'esprit de parti ne corrompaient pas tout ce que cette précieuse liberté a d'estimable."

Candide, apercevant un Milton, lui demanda s'il ne regardait pas cet auteur comme un grand homme. "Qui? dit Pococuranté, ce barbare qui fait un long commentaire du premier chapitre de la Genèse en dix livres de vers durs? ce grossier imitateur des Grecs, qui défigure la création, et qui, tandis que Moïse représente l'Être éternel produisant le monde par la parole, fait prendre un grand compas par le Messiah dans une armoire du ciel pour tracer son ouvrage? Moi, j'estimerais celui qui a gâté l'enfer et le diable du Tasse; qui déguise Lucifer tantôt en crapaud, tantôt en pygmée; qui lui fait rebattre cent fois les mêmes discours; qui le fait disputer sur la théologie; qui, en imitant sérieusement l'invention comique des armes à feu de

[10] The Jacobins were Dominican monks, the order which was charged with the Inquisition.

imagine that I never open them, neither I, nor any-body else."

Martin noticed shelves loaded with English books. "I suppose," he said, "that a republican must enjoy most of those works written so freely." — "Yes," replied Pococuranté; "it is good to write what you think; that's the privilege of man. In all of our Italy, they write only what they don't think; those who inhabit the land of the Caesars and the Antonines dare not have an idea without the permission of a Jacobin.[10] I would be sat-isfied with the freedom that inspires English geniuses if passion and the spirit of faction did not corrupt all that is estimable in this precious liberty."

Candide, noticing a Milton, asked him if he did not consider that author a great man. "Who?" said Poco-curanté, "that barbarian who writes a long commentary on the first chapter of Genesis in ten books of harsh verses? That crude imitator of the Greeks, who disfig-ures Creation, and who, while Moses represents the Eternal Being as producing the world by the word, has the Messiah take a great compass from a closet in heaven to trace his work? I should esteem the one who spoiled the hell and devil of Tasso? Who disguises Lucifer sometimes as a toad, sometimes as a pigmy? Who has him repeat the same speeches a hundred times? Who makes him argue about theology? Who, seriously imitating the comical invention of firearms

l'Arioste, fait tirer le canon dans le ciel par les diables? Ni moi ni personne en Italie n'a pu se plaire à toutes ces tristes extravagances. Le mariage du Péché et de la Mort, et les couleuvres dont le Péché accouche, font vomir tout homme qui a le goût un peu délicat, et sa longue description d'un hôpital n'est bonne que pour un fossoyeur. Ce poème obscur, bizarre et dégoûtant fut méprisé à sa naissance; je le traite aujourd'hui comme il fut traité dans sa patrie par les contemporains. Au reste, je dis ce que je pense, et je me soucie fort peu que les autres pensent comme moi." Candide était affligé de ces discours; il respectait Homère, il aimait un peu Milton. "Hélas! dit-il tout bas à Martin, j'ai bien peur que cet homme-ci n'ait un souverain mépris pour nos poètes allemands. — Il n'y aurait pas grand mal à cela, dit Martin. — Oh! quel homme supérieur! disait encore Candide entre ses dents, quel grand génie que ce Pococuranté! rien ne peut lui plaire."

Après avoit fait ainsi la revue de tous les livres, ils descendirent dans le jardin. Candide en loua toutes les beautés. "Je ne sais rien de si mauvais goût, dit le maître; nous n'avons ici que des colifichets: mais je vais dès demain en faire planter un d'un dessin plus noble." [11]

Quand les deux curieux eurent pris congé de Son Excellence: "Or çà, dit Candide à Martin, vous con-

[11] In his fine critical edition of *Candide*, André Morize suggests that Voltaire is here alluding to his move from Les Délices

in Ariosto, has the devils fire cannon in heaven? Neither I, nor anyone in Italy, has been able to enjoy all these sad extravagances. The marriage of Sin and Death, and the adders to which Sin gives birth, makes any man vomit who has any delicacy of taste; and his long description of a hospital is good only for a grave-digger. This obscure, bizarre, and disgusting poem was despised at its birth; I am treating it today as it was treated in its country by its contemporaries. In any case, I say what I think, and I care very little whether others think like me." Candide was distressed by these observations; he respected Homer, and he rather liked Milton. "Alas!" he said to Martin very softly, "I'm very much afraid that this man would have a sovereign contempt for our German poets." — "There wouldn't be any great harm in that," said Martin. — "Oh! What a superior man!" Candide went on under his breath. "What a great genius, this Pococuranté! Nothing can please him."

After they had thus passed all the books in review, they went down into the garden. Candide praised all its beauties. "I know of nothing in such bad taste," said the master; "we have nothing but tinsel here, but starting tomorrow I will have one planted on a nobler design." [11]

When the two inquisitive visitors had taken leave of His Excellency, Candide said to Martin: "Now,

to Ferney, from the regular gardens of the first to the more rustic aspect of the second.

viendrez que voilà le plus heureux de tous les hommes, car il est au-dessus de tout ce qu'il possède. — Ne voyez-vous pas, dit Martin, qu'il est dégoûté de tout ce qu'il possède? Platon a dit, il y a longtemps, que les meilleurs estomacs ne sont pas ceux qui rebutent tous les aliments. — Mais, dit Candide, n'y a-t-il pas du plaisir à tout critiquer, à sentir des défauts où les autres hommes croient voir des beautés? — C'est-à-dire, reprit Martin, qu'il y a du plaisir à n'avoir pas de plaisir? — Oh bien! dit Candide, il n'y a donc d'heureux que moi, quand je reverrai Mademoiselle Cunégonde. — C'est toujours bien fait d'espérer," dit Martin.[12]

Cependant les jours, les semaines, s'écoulaient; Cacambo ne revenait point, et Candide était si abîmé dans sa douleur qu'il ne fit pas même réflexion que Paquette et frère Giroflée n'étaient pas venus seulement le remercier.

[12] Once again, the allusion to hope (see Chapter 20, note 1).

then, you'll admit that here is the happiest of all men, for he is above everything he owns." — "Don't you see," said Martin, "that he is disgusted with everything he owns? Plato said a long time ago that the best stomachs are not those which reject all foods." — "But," said Candide, "isn't there pleasure in criticizing everything, in sensing defects where other men think they see beauties?" — "That is to say," replied Martin, "that there is pleasure in having no pleasure?" — "Oh well!" said Candide, "there is then no one happy but me, when I see Mademoiselle Cunégonde again." — "It is always good to hope," said Martin.[12]

However, the days, the weeks, went by; Cacambo did not come back, and Candide was so steeped in his sorrow that he did not even notice that Paquette and Friar Giroflée had not even come to thank him.

Chapitre Vingt-sixième

D'un Souper Que Candide et Martin Firent
avec Six Étrangers, et Qui Ils Étaient

Un soir que Candide, suivi de Martin, allait se mettre
à table avec les étrangers qui logeaient dans la même
hôtellerie, un homme à visage couleur de suie l'aborda
par derrière, et, le prenant par le bras, lui dit: "Soyez
prêt à partir avec nous, n'y manquez pas." Il se retourne
et voit Cacambo. Il n'y avait que la vue de Cunégonde
qui pût l'étonner et lui plaire davantage. Il fut sur le
point de devenir fou de joie. Il embrasse son cher ami.
"Cunégonde est ici, sans doute? Où est-elle? Mène-moi
vers elle, que je meure de joie avec elle. — Cunégonde
n'est point ici, dit Cacambo, elle est à Constantinople.
— Ah ciel! à Constantinople! mais, fût-elle à la Chine,
j'y vole, partons. — Nous partirons après souper, reprit
Cacambo; je ne peux vous en dire davantage; je suis
esclave, mon maître m'attend; il faut que j'aille le
servir à table: ne dites mot; soupez, et tenez-vous prêt."

Twenty-sixth Chapter

Of a Supper That Candide and Martin Had with Six Foreigners, and Who They Were

One evening when Candide, followed by Martin, was going to sit down to dinner with the foreigners who were staying in the same hotel, a man with a soot-colored face came up to him from behind, and taking him by the arm, said to him: "Be ready to leave with us, don't fail." He turns around and sees Cacambo. Only the sight of Cunégonde could have surprised and pleased him more. He was ready to go mad with joy. He embraced his dear friend. "Cunégonde is here, no doubt? Where is she? Take me to her, that I may die of joy with her." — "Cunégonde is not here," said Cacambo, "she is in Constantinople." — "Ah heavens! At Constantinople! But were she in China, I'd fly there, let's leave." — "We'll leave after supper," replied Cacambo; "I cannot say anything more to you; I'm a slave, my master is waiting for me; I must go and serve him at table, don't say a word; have supper, and keep yourself ready."

Candide, partagé entre la joie et la douleur, charmé d'avoir revu son agent fidèle, étonné de le voir esclave, plein de l'idée de retrouver sa maîtresse, le cœur agité, l'esprit bouleversé, se mit à table avec Martin, qui voyait de sang-froid toutes ces aventures, et avec six étrangers qui étaient venus passer le carnaval à Venise.

Cacambo, qui versait à boire à l'un de ces étrangers, s'approcha de l'oreille de son maître, sur la fin du repas, et lui dit: "Sire, Votre Majesté partira quand elle voudra, le vaisseau est prêt." Ayant dit ces mots, il sortit. Les convives étonnés, se regardaient sans proférer une seule parole, lorsqu'un autre domestique, s'approchant de son maître, lui dit: "Sire, la chaise de Votre Majesté est à Padoue, et la barque est prête." Le maître fit un signe, et le domestique partit. Tous les convives se regardèrent encore, et la surprise commune redoubla. Un troisième valet, s'approchant aussi d'un troisième étranger, lui dit: "Sire, croyez-moi, Votre Majesté ne doit pas rester ici plus longtemps: je vais tout préparer"; et aussitôt il disparut.

Candide et Martin ne doutèrent pas alors que ce ne fût une mascarade du carnaval. Un quatrième domestique dit au quatrième maître: "Votre Majesté partira quand elle voudra," et sortit comme les autres. Le cinquième valet en dit autant au cinquième maître. Mais le sixième valet parla différemment au sixième étranger, qui était auprès de Candide; il lui dit: "Ma foi, Sire, on ne veut plus faire crédit à Votre Majesté, ni à moi non plus, et nous pourrions bien être coffrés cette nuit, vous et moi; je vais pourvoir à mes affaires:

Candide, torn between joy and sorrow, charmed to see his faithful agent again, astonished to see him a slave, full of the idea of finding his mistress again, his heart agitated, his mind in confusion, sat down to table with Martin who saw all these adventures with coolness, and with six foreigners who had come to spend the Carnival in Venice.

Cacambo, who was pouring drink for one of these foreigners, got his master's ear near the end of the meal, and said to him: "Sire, Your Majesty will leave when you wish, the ship is ready." Having said these words, he went out. The guests, astonished, looked at one another without uttering a single word, when another servant, approaching his master, said to him: "Sire, Your Majesty's chaise is in Padua, and the boat is ready." The master made a sign, and the servant left. All the guests kept looking at each other and the general surprise redoubled. The third valet, also approaching a third foreigner, said to him: "Sire, believe me, Your Majesty must not stay here any longer. I'll go to prepare everything"; and immediately he disappeared.

By now Candide and Martin had no doubt that this was a Carnival masquerade. The fourth servant said to the fourth master: "Your Majesty will leave when you please," and left like the others. The fifth valet said as much to the fifth master. But the sixth valet spoke differently to the sixth stranger, who was next to Candide: "Upon my faith, Sire, they don't want to give Your Majesty any more credit, nor me either, and we'll be locked up tonight, you and I; I'll go look

adieu."

Tous les domestiques ayant disparu, les six étrangers, Candide et Martin demeurèrent dans un profond silence. Enfin Candide le rompit. "Messieurs, dit-il, voilà une singulière plaisanterie. Pourquoi êtes-vous tous rois? Pour moi, je vous avoue que ni moi ni Martin nous ne le sommes."

Le maître de Cacambo prit alors gravement la parole, et dit en italien: "Je ne suis point plaisant, je m'appelle Achmet III;[1] j'ai été grand sultan plusieurs années; je détrônai mon frère; mon neveu m'a détrôné; on a coupé le cou à mes vizirs; j'achève ma vie dans le vieux sérail; mon neveu le grand sultan Mahmoud me permet de voyager quelquefois pour ma santé; et je suis venu passer le carnaval à Venise."

Un jeune homme qui était auprès d'Achmet parla après lui, et dit: "Je m'appelle Ivan;[2] j'ai été empereur de toutes les Russies; j'ai été détrôné au berceau; mon père et ma mère ont été enfermés; on m'a élevé en prison; j'ai quelquefois la permission de voyager, accompagné de ceux qui me gardent; et je suis venu passer le carnaval à Venise."

Le troisième dit: "Je suis Charles-Édouard, roi d'Angleterre;[3] mon père m'a cédé ses droits au royaume;

[1] Ottoman Sultan (1673–1736), who came to the throne in 1703 and was deposed in 1730.

[2] Ivan IV (1740–1764) was proclaimed czar shortly after his birth but deposed in behalf of Elizabeth, daughter of Peter the Great. Ivan was exiled, imprisoned, and then assassinated in 1764 with the connivance of Voltaire's much admired Catherine the Great.

to my own affairs, goodbye."

With all the servants gone, the six foreigners, Candide, and Martin, remained in profound silence. Finally Candide broke it. "Gentlemen," he said, "here's a singular joke. Why, are you all kings? As for myself, I admit that neither I nor Martin is one."

Cacambo's master then gravely spoke up and said in Italian: "I am not joking, my name is Ahmed III; [1] I was Grand Sultan for several years; I dethroned my brother; my nephew dethroned me; they cut my viziers' throats; I am ending my days in the old seraglio; my nephew the Grand Sultan Mahmoud allows me to travel sometimes for my health; and I have come to spend the Carnival in Venice."

A young man who was next to Ahmed spoke after him and said: "My name is Ivan; [2] I was Emperor of all the Russias; I was dethroned in my cradle; my father and mother were locked up; I was raised in prison; I sometimes have permission to travel, accompanied by those who guard me, and I have come to spend the Carnival in Venice."

The third one said: "I am Charles Edward, King of England; [3] my father ceded his rights to the king-

[3] The Young Pretender (1720–88), "Bonnie Prince Charlie," who tried an invasion of Britain in 1745, but was beaten at Culloden and returned abroad. His father was "James III," the Old Pretender (1688–1766), never recognized as king by the British; and his grandfather was James II (1633–1701), who was king of England from 1685 to 1688, but fled during the Glorious Revolution.

j'ai combattu pour les soutenir; on a arraché le cœur à huit cents de mes partisans, et on leur en a battu les joues. J'ai été mis en prison; je vais à Rome faire une visite au roi mon père, détrôné ainsi que moi et mon grand-père; et je suis venu passer le carnaval à Venise."

Le quatrième prit alors la parole et dit: "Je suis roi des Polaques; [4] le sort de la guerre m'a privé de mes États héréditaires; mon père a éprouvé les mêmes revers; je me résigne à la Providence comme le sultan Achmet, l'empereur Ivan et le roi Charles-Édouard, à qui Dieu donne une longue vie; et je suis venu passer le carnaval à Venise."

Le cinquième dit: "Je suis aussi roi des Polaques; [5] j'ai perdu mon royaume deux fois; mais la Providence m'a donné un autre État, dans lequel j'ai fait plus de bien que tous les rois des Sarmates ensemble n'en ont jamais pu faire sur les bords de la Vistule; je me résigne aussi à la Providence; et je suis venu passer le carnaval à Venise."

Il restait au sixième monarque à parler. "Messieurs, dit-il, je ne suis pas si grand seigneur que vous;

[4] Augustus III, elector of Saxony and king of Poland (1696–1763), who was driven from Saxony by Frederick of Prussia in 1756, at the beginning of the Seven Years War. His father was Augustus II (1670–1733), who was only a temporary "exile," between 1706 and 1709, when he had been driven from Poland by the Swedish king Charles XII.

[5] Stanislas I, Stanislas Leszczynski (1677–1766), who was

dom to me; I battled to maintain them; they tore the hearts from eight hundred of my followers, and dashed them in their faces; I was put in prison; I'm going to Rome to pay a visit to the King, my father, dethroned like me and my grandfather; and I have come to spend the Carnival in Venice."

The fourth then took the floor and said: "I am King of the Poles; [4] the fortunes of war have deprived me of my hereditary states; my father underwent the same reverses; I resign myself to Providence like Sultan Ahmed, Emperor Ivan, and King Charles Edward, to whom God may give long life; and I have come to spend the Carnival in Venice."

The fifth said: "I too am King of the Poles; [5] I lost my kingdom twice; but Providence has given me another state in which I have done more good than all the Kings of the Sarmatians together have ever been able to do on the banks of the Vistula. I too resign myself to Providence; and I have come to spend the Carnival in Venice."

It remained for the sixth monarch to speak. "Gentlemen," he said, "I am not as great a lord as you; but

briefly king of Poland twice: once during the exile of Augustus II, and then after Augustus's death in 1733; he was driven out again in 1734, by Augustus III. In 1736 he was given the Duchies of Bar and Lorraine, and ruled his small country with kindness and charm. The father-in-law of France's king Louis xv, and the friend of Voltaire, he was a major figure on the cultural scene of the eighteenth century.

mais enfin j'ai été roi tout comme un autre. Je suis Théodore;[6] on m'a élu roi en Corse; on m'a appelé *Votre Majesté*, et à présent à peine m'appelle-t-on *Monsieur*. J'ai fait frapper de la monnaie, et je ne possède pas un denier; j'ai eu deux secrétaires d'État, et j'ai à peine un valet; je me suis vu sur un trône, et j'ai longtemps été à Londres en prison sur la paille. J'ai bien peur d'être traité de même ici, quoique je sois venu, comme Vos Majestés, passer le carnaval à Venise."

Les cinq autres rois écoutèrent ce discours avec une noble compassion. Chacun d'eux donna vingt sequins[7] au roi Théodore pour avoir des habits et des chemises; Candide lui fit présent d'un diamant de deux mille sequins. "Quel est donc, disaient les cinq rois, ce simple particulier qui est en état de donner cent fois autant que chacun de nous, et qui le donne?"

Dans l'instant qu'on sortait de table, il arriva dans la même hôtellerie quatre Altesses Sérénissimes qui avaient aussi perdu leurs États par le sort de la guerre, et qui venaient passer le reste du carnaval à Venise. Mais Candide ne prit pas seulement garde à ces nouveaux venus. Il n'était occupé que d'aller trouver sa chère Cunégonde à Constantinople.

[6] Theodore, baron von Neuhoff (1670–1756), a German adventurer, who was "king" of Corsica for a few months in 1736,

even so I was king like anyone else; I am Theodore; [6] I was elected King of Corsica; I was called Your Majesty, and now I am hardly called monsieur; I have coined money, and I don't have a penny; I have had two Secretaries of State, and I have hardly one valet; I was on the throne, and for a long time I was in prison in London on straw; I am very much afraid that I will be treated the same way here, although I have come, like Your Majesties, to spend the Carnival in Venice."

The five other kings listened to this speech with noble compassion. Each of them gave twenty sequins [7] to King Theodore to get suits and shirts; Candide gave him a present of a diamond worth two thousand sequins. "Who then is he," said the five kings, "this private individual who is in a position to give a hundred times as much as each of us, and who gives it?"

The moment they were leaving the table, there arrived in the same hotel four Most Serene Highnesses who had also lost their states by the fortune of war, and who were coming to spend the rest of the Carnival in Venice. But Candide did not even take notice of these newcomers. He was occupied only with going to find his dear Cunégonde in Constantinople.

and then expelled by the Genoese.
 [7] A Venetian gold coin.

Chapitre Vingt-septième

Voyage de Candide à Constantinople

Le fidèle Cacambo avait déjà obtenu du patron turc qui allait reconduire le sultan Achmet à Constantinople qu'il recevrait Candide et Martin sur son bord. L'un et l'autre s'y rendirent après s'être prosternés devant Sa misérable Hautesse. Candide, chemin faisant, disait à Martin: "Voilà pourtant six rois détrônés, avec qui nous avons soupé! et encore dans ces six rois il y en a un à qui j'ai fait l'aumône. Peut-être y a-t-il beaucoup d'autres princes plus infortunés. Pour moi, je n'ai perdu que cent moutons, et je vole dans les bras de Cunégonde. Mon cher Martin, encore une fois, Pangloss avait raison, tout est bien. — Je le souhaite, dit Martin. — Mais, dit Candide, voilà une aventure bien peu vraisemblable que nous avons eue à Venise. On n'avait jamais vu ni ouï conter que six rois détrônés soupassent ensemble au cabaret. — Cela n'est pas plus extraordinaire, dit Martin, que la plupart des choses qui nous sont arrivées. Il est très commun que des rois soient détrônés; et à l'égard de l'honneur que nous avons eu de souper avec eux, c'est une bagatelle qui ne mérite pas notre attention."

Twenty-seventh Chapter

Candide's Voyage to Constantinople

The faithful Cacambo had already got the Turkish captain who was going to take Sultan Ahmed back to Constantinople to agree that he would accept Candide and Martin aboard ship. They both came aboard after having prostrated themselves before His miserable Highness. Candide, on the way, said to Martin: "So here were six dethroned kings with whom we had supper! And what's more, among those six kings, there was one to whom I gave alms. Perhaps there are many other even more unfortunate princes. As for me, I've only lost a hundred sheep, and I'm flying to Cunégonde's arms. My dear Martin, once again, Pangloss was right, all is well." — "I hope so," said Martin. — "But," said Candide, "that was a most improbable adventure we had in Venice. No one had ever seen or heard tell of six dethroned kings having supper together at an inn." — "That's no more extraordinary," said Martin, "than most other things that have happened to us. It's quite common for kings to be dethroned; and as for the honor of having had supper with them, that's a detail that doesn't deserve our attention."

A peine Candide fut-il dans le vaisseau qu'il sauta au cou de son ancien valet, de son ami Cacambo. "Eh bien! lui dit-il, que fait Cunégonde? Est-elle toujours un prodige de beauté? M'aime-t-elle toujours? Comment se porte-t-elle? Tu lui as sans doute acheté un palais à Constantinople? — Mon cher maître, répondit Cacambo, Cunégonde lave les écuelles sur le bord de la Propontide,[1] chez un prince qui a très peu d'écuelles; elle est esclave dans la maison d'un ancien souverain, nommé Ragotski,[2] à qui le Grand Turc donne trois écus par jour dans son asile; mais ce qui est bien plus triste, c'est qu'elle a perdu sa beauté et qu'elle est devenue horriblement laide. — Ah! belle ou laide, dit Candide, je suis honnête homme, et mon devoir est de l'aimer toujours. Mais comment peut-elle être réduite à un état si abject avec les cinq ou six millions que tu avais apportés? — Bon, dit Cacambo, ne m'en a-t-il pas fallu donner deux millions au señor don Fernando d'Ibaraa, y Figueora, y Mascarenès, y Lampourdos, y Souza, gouverneur de Buenos-Ayres, pour avoir la permission de reprendre Mademoiselle Cunégonde? Et un pirate ne nous a-t-il pas bravement dépouillés de tout le reste? Ce pirate ne nous a-t-il pas menés au cap de Matapan, à Milo, à Nicarie, à Samos, à Petra, aux Dardanelles, à Marmora, à Scutari? Cunégonde et la vieille servent chez ce prince dont je vous ai parlé, et moi, je suis

[1] The old name for the Sea of Marmora.

[2] Francis Leopold Rakoczy (1676–1735), a Hungarian prince who was elected prince of Transylvania with the help of Louis

Candide was scarcely in the ship when he threw his arms around the neck of his former valet, of his friend Cacambo. "Well!" he said to him, "what is Cunégonde doing? Is she still a prodigy of beauty? Does she still love me? How is she? Doubtless you have bought her a palace in Constantinople?" — "My dear master," replied Cacambo, "Cunégonde is washing dishes on the banks of the Propontis [1] for a prince who has very few dishes; she is a slave in the household of a former sovereign named Rakoczy,[2] whom the Grand Turk gives three écus per day in his refuge; but, what is much sadder is that she has lost her beauty, and has become horribly ugly." — "Ah! beautiful or ugly," said Candide, "I'm an honorable man, and it's my duty to love her always. But how can she be reduced to so abject a condition with the five or six millions that you brought?" — "Well," said Cacambo, "didn't I have to give two millions to Senor Don Fernando d'Ibaraa, y Figueora, y Mascarenes, y Lampourdos, y Souza, Governor of Buenos Aires, to have permission to take Mademoiselle Cunégonde back? And didn't a pirate bravely despoil us of all the rest? And didn't that pirate take us to Cape Matapan, to Milo, to Nicaria, to Samos, to Petra, to the Dardanelles, to Marmora, to Scutari? Cunégonde and the old woman serve the prince whom I have mentioned

XIV in 1704, but was abandoned by his allies and finally fled in 1711. From 1717 to the rest of his life he lived in Turkey.

esclave du sultan détrôné. — Que d'épouvantables calamités enchaînées les unes aux autres! dit Candide. Mais, après tout, j'ai encore quelques diamants; je délivrerai aisément Cunégonde. C'est bien dommage qu'elle soit devenue si laide."

Ensuite, se tournant vers Martin: "Que pensez-vous, dit-il, qui soit le plus à plaindre, de l'empereur Achmet, de l'empereur Ivan, du roi Charles-Édouard, ou de moi? — Je n'en sais rien, dit Martin; il faudrait que je fusse dans vos cœurs pour le savoir. — Ah! dit Candide, si Pangloss était ici, il le saurait et nous l'apprendrait. — Je ne sais, dit Martin, avec quelles balances votre Pangloss aurait pu peser les infortunes des hommes et apprécier leurs douleurs. Tout ce que je présume, c'est qu'il y a des millions d'hommes sur la terre cent fois plus à plaindre que le roi Charles-Édouard, l'empereur Ivan et le sultan Achmet. — Cela pourrait bien être," dit Candide.

On arriva en peu de jours sur le canal de la mer Noire. Candide commença par racheter Cacambo fort cher; et, sans perdre de temps, il se jeta dans une galère, avec ses compagnons, pour aller sur le rivage de la Propontide chercher Cunégonde, quelque laide qu'elle pût être.

Il y avait dans la chiourme deux forçats qui ramaient fort mal, et à qui le levanti patron appliquait de temps en temps quelques coups de nerf de bœuf sur leurs épaules nues; Candide, par un mouvement naturel, les regarda plus attentivement que les autres galériens et s'approcha d'eux avec pitié. Quelques traits de leurs

to you, and I am slave of the dethroned Sultan." —
"What fearful calamities linked one to the other!" said
Candide. "But, after all, I still have a few diamonds;
I'll easily liberate Cunégonde. It's a great pity that
she has become so ugly."

Then, turning toward Martin, he said: "Who do
you think is the most to be pitied, Emperor Ahmed,
Emperor Ivan, King Charles Edward, or I?" — "I have
no idea," said Martin; "I would have to be in your
hearts to know that." — "Ah!" said Candide, "if Pan-
gloss were here, he would know it and tell us." — "I
don't know," said Martin, "with what scales Pangloss
could have weighed the misfortunes of men and esti-
mated their sorrows. All I assume is that there are
millions of men on this earth more to be pitied than
King Charles Edward, Emperor Ivan, and Sultan
Ahmed." — "That could well be," said Candide.

In a few days they reached the Bosporus. First off,
Candide bought Cacambo back at a very high price;
and without wasting time, he threw himself into a
galley with his companions to go to the shores of the
Propontis to find Cunégonde, however ugly she might
be.

In the crew of galley slaves there were two convicts
who rowed very badly, and from time to time the
Levantine captain applied a few strokes of a bull's
pizzle to their naked shoulders; from a natural im-
pulse, Candide looked at them more attentively than
at the other galley slaves, and approached them with
pity. Several features of their disfigured faces seemed

visages défigurés lui parurent avoir un peu de ressemblance avec Pangloss et avec ce malheureux jésuite, ce baron, ce frère de Mademoiselle Cunégonde. Cette idée l'émut et l'attrista. Il les considéra encore plus attentivement. "En vérité, dit-il à Cacambo, si je n'avais pas vu pendre maître Pangloss, et si je n'avais pas eu le malheur de tuer le baron, je croirais que ce sont eux qui rament dans cette galère."

Au nom du baron et de Pangloss les deux forçats poussèrent un grand cri, s'arrêtèrent sur leur banc et laissèrent tomber leurs rames. Le levanti patron accourait sur eux, et les coups de nerf de bœuf redoublaient. "Arrêtez! arrêtez! seigneur, s'écria Candide; je vous donnerai tant d'argent que vous voudrez. — Quoi! c'est Candide! disait l'un des forçats. — Quoi! c'est Candide! disait l'autre. — Est-ce un songe? dit Candide; veillé-je? suis-je dans cette galère? Est-ce là monsieur le baron que j'ai tué? Est-ce là maître Pangloss que j'ai vu pendre? — C'est nous-mêmes, c'est nous-mêmes, répondaient-ils. — Quoi! c'est là ce grand philosophe? disait Martin. — Eh! Monsieur le levanti patron, dit Candide, combien voulez-vous d'argent pour la rançon de Monsieur de Thunder-ten-tronckh, un des premiers barons de l'Empire, et de Monsieur Pangloss, le plus profond métaphysicien d'Allemagne? — Chien de chrétien, répondit le levanti patron, puisque ces deux chiens de forçats chrétiens sont des barons et des métaphysiciens, ce qui est sans doute une grande dignité dans leurs pays, tu m'en donneras cinquante mille sequins. — Vous les aurez, Monsieur;

to him to bear some resemblance to Pangloss and to that unhappy Jesuit, the Baron, Mademoiselle Cunégonde's brother. This idea moved and saddened him. He looked at them even more attentively. "Indeed," he said to Cacambo, "if I had not seen Master Pangloss hanged, and if I had not had the misfortune of killing the Baron, I should think that they are rowing in this galley."

At the words "Baron" and "Pangloss" the two convicts uttered a loud cry, stopped on their bench, and dropped their oars. The Levantine captain ran towards them and the lashes with the bull's pizzle redoubled. "Stop! Stop! sir," Candide exclaimed; "I'll give you as much money as you want." — "What! It's Candide!" said one of the convicts. — "What! It's Candide!" said the other. — "Is it a dream?" said Candide; "am I awake? Am I in this galley? Is this Monsieur the Baron, whom I killed? Is that Master Pangloss, whom I saw hanged?" — "It's us, it's us," they replied. — "What! Is this that great philosopher?" said Martin. — "Ah! Monsieur Levantine captain," said Candide, "how much money do you want for the ransom of Monsieur of Thunder-ten-tronckh, one of the first barons of the empire, and of Monsieur Pangloss, the most profound metaphysician of Germany?" — "Dog of a Christian," replied the Levantine captain, "since these two Christian convict dogs are barons and metaphysicians, which is doubtless a high rank in their country, you will give me fifty thousand sequins for them." — "You shall have them, sir; take me back to

ramenez-moi comme un éclair à Constantinople, et vous serez payé sur-le-champ. Mais non, menez-moi chez Mademoiselle Cunégonde." Le levanti patron, sur la première offre de Candide, avait déjà tourné la proue vers la ville, et il faisait ramer plus vite qu'un oiseau ne fend les airs.

Candide embrassa cent fois le baron et Pangloss. "Et comment ne vous ai-je pas tué, mon cher baron? et, mon cher Pangloss, comment êtes-vous en vie après avoir été pendu? et pourquoi êtes-vous tous deux aux galères en Turquie? — Est-il bien vrai que ma chère sœur soit dans ce pays? disait le baron. — Oui, répondait Cacambo. — Je revois donc mon cher Candide," s'écriait Pangloss. Candide leur présentait Martin et Cacambo. Ils s'embrassaient tous, ils parlaient tous à la fois. La galère volait, ils étaient déjà dans le port. On fit venir un juif, à qui Candide vendit pour cinquante mille sequins un diamant de la valeur de cent mille, et qui lui jura par Abraham qu'il n'en pouvait donner davantage. Il paya incontinent la rançon du baron et de Pangloss. Celui-ci se jeta aux pieds de son libérateur et les baigna de larmes; l'autre le remercia par un signe de tête et lui promit de lui rendre cet argent à la première occasion. "Mais est-il bien possible que ma sœur soit en Turquie? disait-il. — Rien n'est si possible, reprit Cacambo, puisqu'elle écure la vaisselle chez un prince de Transylvanie." On fit aussitôt venir deux juifs; Candide vendit encore des diamants; et ils repartirent tous dans une autre galère pour aller délivrer Cunégonde.

Constantinople like lightning, and you'll be paid on the spot. But no, take me to Mademoiselle Cunégonde." The Levantine captain had already turned his prow toward the city at Candide's first offer, and he had everyone row more swiftly than a bird cleaves the air.

Candide embraced the Baron and Pangloss a hundred times. "And how is it that I didn't kill you, my dear Baron? and my dear Pangloss, how is it that you're alive after being hanged? and why are you both in the galleys in Turkey?" — "Is it really true that my dear sister is in this country?" said the Baron. — "Yes," replied Cacambo. — "So I see my dear Candide again," exclaimed Pangloss. Candide introduced Martin and Cacambo to them. They all embraced; they all talked at once. The galley flew, they were already in port. They sent for a Jew, to whom Candide sold for fifty thousand sequins a diamond worth a hundred thousand, and who swore to him by Abraham that he could not give any more for it. Right off, Candide paid the Baron's and Pangloss's ransom. The latter threw himself at his liberator's feet and bathed them with tears; the other thanked him with a nod, and promised to repay him this money at the first opportunity. "But is it really possible that my sister is in Turkey?" he said. — "Nothing is so possible," retorted Cacambo, "since she is cleaning dishes for a prince of Transylvania." At once they sent for two Jews: Candide sold more diamonds; and they all left once more in another galley to go and deliver Cunégonde.

Chapitre Vingt-huitième

Ce Qui Arriva à Candide, à Cunégonde, à Pangloss, à Martin, etc.

"Pardon, encore une fois, dit Candide au baron; pardon, mon révérend père, de vous avoir donné un grand coup d'épée au travers du corps. — N'en parlons plus, dit le baron; je fus un peu trop vif, je l'avoue; mais, puisque vous voulez savoir par quel hasard vous m'avez vu aux galères, je vous dirai qu'après avoir été guéri de ma blessure par le frère apothicaire du collège, je fus attaqué et enlevé par un parti espagnol; on me mit en prison à Buenos-Ayres dans le temps que ma sœur venait d'en partir. Je demandai à retourner à Rome auprès du père général. Je fus nommé pour aller servir d'aumônier à Constantinople auprès de monsieur l'ambassadeur de France. Il n'y avait pas huit jours que j'étais entré en fonction, quand je trouvai sur le soir un jeune icoglan [1] très bien fait. Il faisait fort chaud: le jeune homme voulut se baigner; je pris cette occasion de me baigner aussi. Je ne savais pas que ce fût un crime capital pour un chrétien d'être trouvé tout nu avec un jeune musulman. Un cadi [2] me fit donner cent

[1] A sultan's page.

Twenty-eighth Chapter

What Happened to Candide, to Cunégonde, to Pangloss, to Martin, etc.

"Forgive me, once again," Candide said to the Baron; "forgive me, Reverend Father, for having given you a great sword thrust through the body." — "Let's talk no more about it," said the Baron; "I was a little too hasty, I'll admit; but since you want to know by what accident you saw me in the galleys, I'll tell you that after I was cured of my wound by Brother Apothecary of the College, I was attacked and carried off by a party of Spaniards; they put me in prison in Buenos Aires at the time my sister had just left. I asked to return to Rome, to the Father General. I was appointed to go and serve as Almoner in Constantinople, to monsieur the Ambassador of France. Not a week after I had taken up my duties, it happened one evening that I met a young, very handsome icoglan.[1] It was very hot: the young man wanted to bathe; I took this opportunity to bathe too. I didn't know that it was a capital crime for a Christian to be found stark naked with a young Muslim. A cadi [2] sentenced me

[2] A muslim judge.

coups de bâton sous la plante des pieds et me con-
damna aux galères. Je ne crois pas qu'on ait fait une
plus horrible injustice. Mais je voudrais bien savoir
pourquoi ma sœur est dans la cuisine d'un souverain
de Transylvanie réfugié chez les Turcs."

"Mais vous, mon cher Pangloss, dit Candide, com-
ment se peut-il que je vous revoie? — Il est vrai, dit
Pangloss, que vous m'avez vu pendre; je devais naturel-
lement être brûlé; mais vous vous souvenez qu'il plut
à verse lorsqu'on allait me cuire: l'orage fut si violent
qu'on désespéra d'allumer le feu; je fus pendu, parce
qu'on ne put mieux faire: un chirurgien acheta mon
corps, m'emporta chez lui et me disséqua. Il me fit
d'abord une incision cruciale depuis le nombril jusqu'à
la clavicule. On ne pouvait pas avoir été plus mal
pendu que je l'avais été. L'exécuteur des hautes œuvres
de la sainte Inquisition, lequel était sous-diacre, brûlait
à la vérité les gens à merveille, mais il n'était pas ac-
coutumé à pendre: la corde était mouillée et glissa mal,
elle fut nouée; enfin je respirais encore: l'incision cru-
ciale me fit jeter un si grand cri que mon chirurgien
tomba à la renverse, et, croyant qu'il disséquait le
diable, il s'enfuit en mourant de peur, et tomba encore
sur l'escalier en fuyant. Sa femme accourut au bruit,
d'un cabinet voisin; elle me vit sur la table étendu
avec mon incision cruciale: elle eut encore plus de peur
que son mari, s'enfuit, et tomba sur lui. Quand ils
furent un peu revenus à eux, j'entendis la chirurgienne
qui disait au chirurgien: 'Mon bon, de quoi vous avisez-
vous aussi de disséquer un hérétique? Ne savez-vous

to a hundred strokes on the soles of my feet, and condemned me to the galleys. I don't think a more horrible injustice has ever been done. But I'd very much like to know why my sister is in the kitchen of a sovereign of Transylvania exiled among the Turks."

"But you, my dear Pangloss," said Candide, "how can it be that I see you again?" — "It's true," said Pangloss, "that you saw me hanged; naturally I should have been burned, but you'll remember that it poured just when they were about to cook me: the downpour was so violent that they despaired of lighting the fire; I was hanged because they couldn't do any better: a surgeon bought my body, took me home, and dissected me. First he made a cross-shaped incision in me, from the navel to the clavicle. One couldn't have been hanged worse than I had been. The Executor of High Works of the Inquisition, who was a subdeacon, in fact burned people marvelously, but he was not accustomed to hanging: the rope was moist and slipped badly, it became knotted; in a word, I was still breathing; the cross-shaped incision made me scream such a big scream that my surgeon fell over backward; and, thinking that he was dissecting the devil, he fled, dying of fear, and then fell on the staircase as he fled. His wife came running from a nearby room at the noise; she saw me stretched out on the table with my cross-shaped incision; she was even more afraid than her husband, fled, and fell on top of him. When they had recovered a little, I heard the surgeon's wife say to the surgeon: 'My dear, what are you thinking of, dissecting a heretic? Don't you know that the devil al-

pas que le diable est toujours dans le corps de ces gens-là? Je vais vite chercher un prêtre pour l'exorciser.' Je frémis à ce propos, et je ramassai le peu de forces qui me restaient pour crier: 'Ayez pitié de moi!' Enfin le barbier portugais [3] s'enhardit; il recousit ma peau; sa femme même eut soin de moi; je fus sur pied au bout de quinze jours. Le barbier me trouva une condition, et me fit laquais d'un chevalier de Malte qui allait à Venise; mais mon maître n'ayant pas de quoi me payer, je me mis au service d'un marchand vénitien, et je le suivis à Constantinople.

"Un jour il me prit fantaisie d'entrer dans une mosquée; il n'y avait qu'un vieux iman et une jeune dévote très jolie qui disait ses patenôtres; sa gorge était toute découverte: elle avait entre ses deux tétons un beau bouquet de tulipes, de roses, d'anémones, de renoncules, d'hyacinthes et d'oreilles-d'ours; elle laissa tomber son bouquet; je le ramassai, et je le lui remis avec un empressement très respectueux. Je fus si long-temps à le lui remettre que l'iman se mit en colère, et, voyant que j'étais chrétien, il cria à l'aide. On me mena chez le cadi, qui me fit donner cent coups de latte sur la plante des pieds et m'envoya aux galères. Je fus enchaîné précisément dans la même galère et au même banc que monsieur le baron. Il y avait dans cette galère quatre jeunes gens de Marseille, cinq prêtres napoli-tains, et deux moines de Corfou, qui nous dirent que

[3] In the first half of the eighteenth century, the French surgeons finally liberated themselves from their humiliating association with the Barbers' Guild.

ways possesses these people? I'll run get a priest to exorcise him.' I shuddered at this suggestion and gathered up the little strength I had left to exclaim: 'Have pity on me!' Finally the Portuguese barber [3] grew more daring: he sewed up my skin; his wife even took care of me; I was on my feet after two weeks. The barber found me a job, and made me lackey of a Knight of Malta who was going to Venice; but since my master had no money to pay me, I entered the service of a Venetian merchant, and I followed him to Constantinople.

"One day I got the notion I'd enter a mosque; only an old imam was there and a young, very pretty devotee who was saying her Lord's Prayer; her bosom was fully uncovered: she had between her two breasts a beautiful bouquet of tulips, roses, anemones, buttercups, hyacinths, and auriculos; she dropped her bouquet; I picked it up, and put it back for her with a most respectful eagerness. I took such a long time putting it back that the imam got angry, and, noticing that I was a Christian, he called for help. They brought me before the cadi, who sentenced me to a hundred strokes on the soles of my feet, and sent me to the galleys. I was chained precisely in the same galley and to the same bench as Monsieur the Baron. There were in that galley four young men from Marseilles, five Neapolitan priests, and two monks from Corfu, who

de pareilles aventures arrivaient tous les jours. Monsieur le baron prétendait qu'il avait essuyé une plus grande injustice que moi; je prétendais, moi, qu'il était beaucoup plus permis de remettre un bouquet sur la gorge d'une femme que d'être tout nu avec un icoglan. Nous disputions sans cesse, et nous recevions vingt coups de nerf de bœuf par jour, lorsque l'enchaînement des événements de cet univers vous a conduit dans notre galère, et que vous nous avez rachetés."

"Eh bien! mon cher Pangloss, lui dit Candide, quand vous avez été pendu, disséqué, roué de coups, et que vous avez ramé aux galères, avez-vous toujours pensé que tout allait le mieux du monde? — Je suis toujours de mon premier sentiment, répondit Pangloss, car enfin je suis philosophe: il ne me convient pas de me dédire, Leibnitz ne pouvant pas avoir tort, et l'harmonie préétablie étant d'ailleurs la plus belle chose du monde, aussi bien que le plein et la matière subtile."

told us that similar adventures happened every day. Monsieur the Baron claimed that he had suffered a greater injustice than I; as for me, I claimed that it was much more permissible to put a bouquet back into a woman's bosom than to be stark naked with an icoglan. We were arguing without ceasing, and were receiving twenty strokes per day with a bull's pizzle, when the chain of events in this universe brought you to our galley, and you ransomed us."

"Well, my dear Pangloss," Candide said to him, "when you were being hanged, dissected, unmercifully beaten, and rowing in the galleys, did you continue to think that all is for the best in this world?" — "I retain my original view," Pangloss replied; "for, after all, I'm a philosopher: it's improper for me to recant, since Leibnitz cannot be wrong, and since, anyway, pre-established harmony is the finest thing in the world, as is the plenum and subtle matter."

Chapitre Vingt-neuvième

Comment Candide Retrouva Cunégonde et la Vieille

Pendant que Candide, le baron, Pangloss, Martin et Cacambo contaient leurs aventures, qu'ils raisonnaient sur les événements contingents ou non contingents de cet univers, qu'ils disputaient sur les effets et les causes, sur le mal moral et sur le mal physique, sur la liberté et la nécessité, sur les consolations que l'on peut éprouver lorsqu'on est aux galères en Turquie, ils abordèrent sur le rivage de la Propontide à la maison du prince de Transylvanie. Les premiers objets qui se présentèrent furent Cunégonde et la vieille, qui étendaient des serviettes sur des ficelles pour les faire sécher.

Le baron pâlit à cette vue. Le tendre amant Candide, en voyant sa belle Cunégonde rembrunie, les yeux éraillés, la gorge sèche, les joues ridées, les bras rouges et écaillés, recula trois pas, saisi d'horreur, et avança ensuite par bon procédé. Elle embrassa Candide et son frère; on embrassa la vieille: Candide les racheta toutes deux.

Il y avait une petite métairie dans le voisinage; la

Twenty-ninth Chapter

How Candide Found Cunégonde and the Old Woman Again

While Candide, the Baron, Pangloss, Martin, and Cacambo were recounting their adventures, reasoning about the contingent and noncontingent events in this universe, arguing about causes and effects, about moral evil and physical evil, about free will and necessity, about the consolations one may find when one is in the galleys in Turkey, they landed on the shore of Propontis, at the house of the prince of Transylvania. The first objects that met their eyes were Cunégonde and the old woman, who were spreading out towels to dry on the lines.

The Baron paled at this sight. Candide, the tender lover, seeing his beautiful Cunégonde all brown, eyes bloodshot, flat-chested, cheeks wrinkled, arms red and chapped, recoiled three paces, seized with horror, and then advanced out of politeness. She embraced Candide and her brother; they embraced the old woman: Candide ransomed them both.

There was a little farm in the neighborhood; the

vieille proposa à Candide de s'en accommoder, en attendant que toute la troupe eût une meilleure destinée.
Cunégonde ne savait pas qu'elle était enlaidie, personne
ne l'en avait avertie: elle fit souvenir Candide de ses
promesses avec un ton si absolu que le bon Candide
n'osa pas la refuser. Il signifia donc au baron qu'il allait
se marier avec sa sœur. "Je ne souffrirai jamais, dit le
baron, une telle bassesse de sa part et une telle insolence
de la vôtre; cette infamie ne me sera jamais reprochée:
les enfants de ma sœur ne pourraient entrer dans les
chapitres d'Allemagne.[1] Non, jamais ma sœur n'épousera qu'un baron de l'Empire." Cunégonde se jeta à
ses pieds et les baigna de larmes; il fut inflexible.
"Maître fou, lui dit Candide, je t'ai réchappé des
galères, j'ai payé ta rançon, j'ai payé celle de ta sœur;
elle lavait ici des écuelles, elle est laide, j'ai la bonté
d'en faire ma femme, et tu prétends encore t'y opposer!
Je te retuerais si j'en croyais ma colère. — Tu peux
me tuer encore, dit le baron, mais tu n'épouseras pas
ma sœur de mon vivant."

[1] Assemblies of the German nobility.

old woman suggested to Candide that he acquire it until the whole group should enjoy better fortunes. Cunégonde did not know that she had grown ugly, nobody had told her so: she reminded Candide of his promises in so peremptory a tone that the good Candide did not dare refuse her. So he informed the Baron that he was going to marry his sister. "I'll never stand for such a sordid act on her part," said the Baron, "and such insolence on yours; I shall never be reproached with this infamy: my sister's children wouldn't be able to enter the Chapters of Germany.[1] No, my sister shall never marry anyone but a Baron of the Empire." Cunégonde threw herself at his feet, and bathed them with tears; he was inflexible. "You supreme madman," Candide said to him, "I rescued you from the galleys, I paid your ransom, I paid your sister's; she was washing dishes here, she is ugly, I have the decency to make her my wife; and you still dare to oppose it! I'd kill you again if I listened to my anger." — "You may kill me again," said the Baron, "but you won't marry my sister while I'm alive."

Chapitre Trentième

Conclusion

Candide, dans le fond de son cœur, n'avait aucune envie d'épouser Cunégonde. Mais l'impertinence extrême du baron le déterminait à conclure le mariage, et Cunégonde le pressait si vivement qu'il ne pouvait s'en dédire. Il consulta Pangloss, Martin, et le fidèle Cacambo. Pangloss fit un beau mémoire par lequel il prouvait que le baron n'avait nul droit sur sa sœur, et qu'elle pouvait, selon toutes les lois de l'Empire, épouser Candide de la main gauche.[1] Martin conclut à jeter le baron dans la mer; Cacambo décida qu'il fallait le rendre au levanti patron et le remettre aux galères; après quoi on l'enverrait à Rome au père général par le premier vaisseau. L'avis fut trouvé fort bon; la vieille l'approuva; on n'en dit rien à sa sœur; la chose fut exécutée pour quelque argent, et on eut le plaisir d'attraper un jésuite et de punir l'orgueil d'un baron allemand.

[1] A morganatic marriage; a marriage between a noble and a commoner, which conferred noble rights neither on the wife nor on the children.

Thirtieth Chapter

Conclusion

At the bottom of his heart Candide had no desire whatever to marry Cunégonde; but the Baron's extreme impertinence determined him to conclude the marriage, and Cunégonde urged him so strongly that he could not retract. He consulted Pangloss, Martin, and the faithful Cacambo. Pangloss wrote a fine memorandum in which he proved that the Baron had no rights over his sister, and that she could, according to all the laws of the Empire, make a left-handed marriage [1] with Candide. Martin recommended that the Baron should be thrown into the sea; Cacambo decided that he should be returned to the Levantine captain and put back in the galleys, after which he would be sent to Rome to the Father General by the first ship. This was thought to be very good advice; the old woman approved it; they said nothing about it to his sister; the matter was carried out with a little money, and they had the pleasure of tricking a Jesuit and punishing the pride of a German Baron.

Il était tout naturel d'imaginer qu'après tant de désastres Candide, marié avec sa maîtresse et vivant avec le philosophe Pangloss, le philosophe Martin, le prudent Cacambo, et la vieille, ayant d'ailleurs rapporté tant de diamants de la patrie des anciens Incas, mènerait la vie du monde la plus agréable; mais il fut tant friponné par les juifs qu'il ne lui resta plus rien que sa petite métairie;[2] sa femme, devenant tous les jours plus laide, devint acariâtre et insupportable; la vieille était infirme et fut encore de plus mauvaise humeur que Cunégonde. Cacambo, qui travaillait au jardin et qui allait vendre des légumes à Constantinople, était excédé de travail et maudissait sa destinée. Pangloss était au désespoir de ne pas briller dans quelque université d'Allemagne. Pour Martin, il était fermement persuadé qu'on est également mal partout; il prenait les choses en patience. Candide, Martin, et Pangloss disputaient quelquefois de métaphysique et de morale. On voyait souvent passer sous les fenêtres de la métairie des bateaux chargés d'effendis, de bachas,[3] de cadis, qu'on envoyait en exil à Lemnos, à Mitylène, à Erzeroum; on voyait venir d'autres cadis, d'autres bachas, d'autres effendis, qui prenaient la place des expulsés et qui étaient expulsés à leur tour. On voyait des têtes proprement empaillées qu'on allait présenter à la Sublime Porte. Ces spectacles faisaient redoubler les dissertations; et quand on ne disputait pas, l'ennui

[2] This reflects Voltaire's own experiences with Jewish bankers, combined with his inability to rise above the current anti-Jewish prejudices of his day, which such *philosophes* as Mon-

It was quite natural to suppose that after so many disasters Candide, married to his mistress and living with the philosopher Pangloss, the philosopher Martin, the prudent Cacambo, and the old woman, having in addition brought back so many diamonds from the country of the ancient Incas, would lead the most pleasant life in the world; but he was so cheated by the Jews that nothing remained to him beside his little farm; [2] his wife, growing uglier every day, grew shrewish and insufferable; the old woman was ailing and was even more ill-tempered than Cunégonde. Cacambo, who worked in the garden and went to sell vegetables in Constantinople, was overworked and cursed his lot. Pangloss was in despair at not shining in some university in Germany. As for Martin, he was firmly convinced that people are equally miserable everywhere; he took things patiently. Candide, Martin, and Pangloss sometimes argued about metaphysics and morals. Often they saw ships passing under the windows of the farm, laden with effendis, pashas,[3] cadis, who were being sent into exile at Lemnos, Mitylene, Erzerum; they saw other cadis arriving, other pashas, other effendis, who were taking the place of the exiles, and who were exiled in their turn. They saw heads properly empaled on their way to be presented to the Sublime Porte. These sights redoubled their discussions; and when they were not arguing, boredom was

tesquieu and Lessing had managed to overcome.

[3] The first is an honorific Turkish title; the second a Turkish governor.

était si excessif que la vieille osa un jour leur dire: "Je voudrais savoir lequel est le pire, ou d'être violée cent fois par des pirates nègres, d'avoir une fesse coupée, de passer par les baguettes chez les Bulgares, d'être fouetté et pendu dans un auto-da-fé, d'être disséqué, de ramer en galère, d'éprouver enfin toutes les misères par lesquelles nous avons tous passé, ou bien de rester ici à ne rien faire? — C'est une grande question," dit Candide.

Ce discours fit naître de nouvelles réflexions, et Martin surtout conclut que l'homme était né pour vivre dans les convulsions de l'inquiétude, ou dans la léthargie de l'ennui. Candide n'en convenait pas, mais il n'assurait rien. Pangloss avouait qu'il avait toujours horriblement souffert; mais, ayant soutenu une fois que tout allait à merveille, il le soutenait toujours, et n'en croyait rien.

Une chose acheva de confirmer Martin dans ses détestables principes, de faire hésiter plus que jamais Candide et d'embarrasser Pangloss. C'est qu'ils virent un jour aborder dans leur métairie Paquette et le frère Giroflée, qui étaient dans la plus extrême misère; ils avaient bien vite mangé leurs trois mille piastres, s'étaient quittés, s'étaient raccommodés, s'étaient brouillés, avaient été mis en prison, s'étaient enfuis, et enfin frère Giroflée s'était fait Turc. Paquette continuait son métier partout et n'y gagnait plus rien. "Je l'avais bien prévu, dit Martin à Candide, que vos présents seraient bientôt dissipés et ne les rendraient que plus misérables. Vous avez regorgé de millions de

so excessive that the old woman dared to say to them one day: "I'd like to know which is worse: to be raped a hundred times by Negro pirates, to have a buttock cut off, to run the gauntlet among the Bulgarians, to be flogged and hanged in an auto-da-fé, to be dissected, to row in the galleys, in a word to undergo all the miseries we have suffered, or rather to stay here and do nothing?" — "That's a great question," said Candide.

This speech called forth new reflections, and Martin above all concluded that man was born to live in the convulsions of anxiety, or in the lethargy of boredom. Candide did not agree with that, but he asserted nothing. Pangloss admitted that he had always suffered horribly; but having once maintained that all was wonderful, he continued to maintain it and did not believe it.

One thing finally confirmed Martin in his detestable principles, made Candide hesitate more than ever, and embarrassed Pangloss. One day they saw Paquette and Friar Giroflée approach their farm; they were in the most extreme misery; they had very quickly gone through their three thousand piastres, had left each other, made up, quarreled, been put in prison; had escaped, and finally Friar Giroflée had turned Turk. Paquette continued her trade everywhere, and no longer earned anything with it. "I foresaw very well," Martin said to Candide, "that your presents would soon be dissipated and would only make them more miserable. You were once bloated with millions of

piastres, vous et Cacambo, et vous n'êtes pas plus heureux que frère Giroflée et Paquette. — Ah! ah! dit Pangloss à Paquette, le Ciel vous ramène donc ici parmi nous, ma pauvre enfant? Savez-vous bien que vous m'avez coûté le bout du nez, un œil et une oreille? Comme vous voilà faite! eh! qu'est-ce que ce monde!" Cette nouvelle aventure les engagea à philosopher plus que jamais.

Il y avait dans le voisinage un derviche très fameux, qui passait pour le meilleur philosophe de la Turquie; ils allèrent le consulter; Pangloss porta la parole, et lui dit: "Maître, nous venons vous prier de nous dire pourquoi un aussi étrange animal que l'homme a été formé. — De quoi te mêles-tu? lui dit le derviche; est-ce là ton affaire? — Mais, mon révérend père, dit Candide, il y a horriblement de mal sur la terre. — Qu'importe, dit le derviche, qu'il y ait du mal ou du bien? Quand Sa Hautesse envoie un vaisseau en Egypte, s'embarrasse-t-elle si les souris qui sont dans le vaisseau sont à leur aise ou non? — Que faut-il donc faire? dit Pangloss. — Te taire, dit le derviche. — Je me flattais, dit Pangloss, de raisonner un peu avec vous des effets et des causes, du meilleur des mondes possibles, de l'origine du mal, de la nature de l'âme, et de l'harmonie préétablie." Le derviche, à ces mots, leur ferma la porte au nez.

Pendant cette conversation, la nouvelle s'était répandue qu'on venait d'étrangler à Constantinople deux vizirs du banc et le muphti, et qu'on avait empalé plusieurs de leurs amis. Cette catastrophe faisait partout un grand bruit pendant quelques heures. Pangloss,

piastres, you and Cacambo, and you are no happier than Friar Giroflée and Paquette." — "Ah! Ah!" Pangloss said to Paquette, "so heaven brings you back among us here, my poor child! Do you know that you cost me the end of my nose, an eye, and an ear? Now look at you! Eh! What a world this is!" This new adventure set them to philosophizing more than ever.

There was a very famous dervish in the neighborhood who was supposed to be the best philosopher in Turkey; they went to consult him; Pangloss was spokesman, and said to him: "Master, we come to ask you to tell us why so strange an animal as man was created." — "What are you meddling in?" the dervish said to him; "is that your business?" — "But, Reverend Father," said Candide, "there is a horrible lot of evil in the world." — "What does it matter," said the dervish, "whether there is evil or good? When His Highness sends a ship to Egypt, does he worry whether the mice in the ship are comfortable or not?" — "What, then, must we do?" said Pangloss. "Be silent," said the dervish. — "I flattered myself," said Pangloss, "that I might briefly discuss causes and effects with you, the best of possible worlds, the origin of evil, the nature of the soul, and pre-established harmony." At these words the dervish shut the door in their faces.

During the conversation the news had spread that in Constantinople they had just strangled two viziers of the Divan and the Mufti, and that they had impaled several of their friends. This catastrophe caused a great stir everywhere for a few hours. Pangloss, Can-

Candide, et Martin, en retournant à la petite métairie, rencontrèrent un bon vieillard qui prenait le frais à sa porte sous un berceau d'orangers. Pangloss, qui était aussi curieux que raisonneur, lui demanda comment se nommait le muphti qu'on venait d'étrangler. "Je n'en sais rien, répondit le bonhomme, et je n'ai jamais su le nom d'aucun muphti ni d'aucun vizir. J'ignore absolument l'aventure dont vous me parlez; je présume qu'en général ceux qui se mêlent des affaires publiques périssent quelquefois misérablement, et qu'ils le méritent; mais je ne m'informe jamais de ce qu'on fait à Constantinople; je me contente d'y envoyer vendre les fruits du jardin que je cultive." Ayant dit ces mots, il fit entrer les étrangers dans sa maison: ses deux filles et ses deux fils leur présentèrent plusieurs sortes de sorbets qu'ils faisaient eux-mêmes, du kaïmac [4] piqué d'écorce de cédrat confit, des oranges, des citrons, des limons, des ananas, des pistaches, du café de Moka qui n'était point mêlé avec le mauvais café de Batavia et des îles.[5] Après quoi les deux filles de ce bon musulman parfumèrent les barbes de Candide, de Pangloss, et de Martin.

"Vous devez avoir, dit Candide au Turc, une vaste et magnifique terre? — Je n'ai que vingt arpents, répondit le Turc; je les cultive avec mes enfants; le travail éloigne de nous trois grands maux: l'ennui, le vice, et le besoin."

Candide, en retournant dans sa métairie, fit de pro-

[4] Turkish sherbet.

dide, and Martin, returning to the little farm, met a good old man who was enjoying the fresh air under a bower of orange trees. Pangloss, who was as curious as he was argumentative, asked him the name of the Mufti who had just been strangled. "I have no idea," replied the good man; "and I've never known the name of any mufti or any vizier. I know absolutely nothing of the adventure you are telling me about; I assume that in general those who meddle with public affairs sometimes perish miserably, and that they deserve it; but I never try to find out what is going on in Constantinople; I content myself with sending there to sell the fruits of the garden I cultivate." Having said these words, he had the strangers come into his house; his two daughters and two sons presented them with several kinds of sherbet which they made themselves, kaimak [4] flavored with candied citron peel, oranges, lemons, limes, pineapples, pistachios, Mocha coffee that had not been mixed with the bad coffee of Batavia and the Islands.[5] After which the two daughters of this good Muslim perfumed the beards of Candide, Pangloss, and Martin.

"You must have," Candide said to the Turk, "a vast and magnificent property?" — "I have only twenty acres," replied the Turk; "I cultivate them with my children; work keeps away from us three great evils: boredom, vice, and need."

As Candide returned to his farm, he reflected deeply

[5] That is, the West Indies.

fondes réflexions sur le discours du Turc. Il dit à Pangloss et à Martin: "Ce bon vieillard me paraît s'être fait un sort bien préférable à celui des six rois avec qui nous avons eu l'honneur de souper. — Les grandeurs, dit Pangloss, sont fort dangereuses, selon le rapport de tous les philosophes: car enfin Églon, roi des Moabites, fut assassiné par Aod; Absalon fut pendu par les cheveux et percé de trois dards; le roi Nadab, fils de Jéroboam, fut tué par Baasa; le roi Éla, par Zambri; Ochosias, par Jéhu; Athalia, par Joïada; les rois Joachim, Jéchonias, Sédécias, furent esclaves.[6] Vous savez comment périrent Crésus, Astyage, Darius, Denys de Syracuse, Pyrrhus, Persée, Annibal, Jugurtha, Arioviste, César, Pompée, Néron, Othon, Vitellius, Domitien, Richard II d'Angleterre, Édouard II, Henri VI, Richard III, Marie Stuart, Charles I[er], les trois Henri de France, l'empereur Henri IV?[7] Vous savez . . . — Je sais aussi, dit Candide, qu'il faut cultiver notre jardin. — Vous avez raison, dit Pangloss: car, quand l'homme fut mis dans le jardin d'Éden, il y fut mis *ut operaretur eum*, pour qu'il travaillât; ce qui prouve que l'homme n'est pas né pour le repos. — Travaillons sans raisonner, dit Martin; c'est le seul moyen de rendre la vie supportable."

Toute la petite société entra dans ce louable dessein; chacun se mit à exercer ses talents. La petite terre

[6] The kings here referred to can be found in the books of Judges, Samuel, and Kings (see Introduction, pp. xx–xxi).

on the Turk's observations. He said to Pangloss and to Martin: "That good old man seems to me to have made for himself a lot far preferable to that of the six kings with whom we had the honor of dining." — "Greatness," said Pangloss, "is very dangerous, according to the account of all the philosophers: for after all, Eglon, King of the Moabites, was assassinated by Ehud; Absalom was hanged by his hair and pierced by three darts; King Nadab, son of Jeroboam, was killed by Baasha; King Elah by Zimri; Ahaziah by Jehu; Athaliah by Jehoiada; Kings Jehoiakim, Jeconiah, and Zedekiah were made into slaves.[6] You know how Croesus perished, Astyages, Darius, Dionysius of Syracuse, Pyrrhus, Perseus, Hannibal, Jugurtha, Ariovistus, Caesar, Pompey, Nero, Otho, Vitellius, Domitian, Richard ii of England, Edward ii, Henry vi, Richard iii, Mary Stuart, Charles i, the three Henrys of France, the Emperor Henry iv?[7] You know . . ." — "I also know," said Candide, "that we must cultivate our garden." — "You are right," said Pangloss; "for when man was put into the Garden of Eden, he was put there *ut operaretur eum*, to work; which proves that man was not born for rest." — "Let us work without arguing," said Martin; "it's the only way to make life endurable."

The whole little society entered into this praiseworthy plan; each started to exercise his talents. The

[7] All these rulers came to a bad end: deposed, exiled, assassinated, or executed.

rapporta beaucoup. Cunégonde était à la vérité bien laide, mais elle devint une excellente pâtissière; Paquette broda; la vieille eut soin du linge. Il n'y eut pas jusqu'à frère Giroflée qui ne rendît service; il fut un très bon menuisier, et même devint honnêtc homme; et Pangloss disait quelquefois à Candide: "Tous les événements sont enchaînés dans le meilleur des mondes possibles: car enfin, si vous n'aviez pas été chassé d'un beau château à grands coups de pied dans le derrière pour l'amour de Mademoiselle Cunégonde, si vous n'aviez pas été mis à l'Inquisition, si vous n'aviez pas couru l'Amérique à pied, si vous n'aviez pas perdu tous vos moutons du bon pays d'Eldorado, vous ne mangeriez pas ici des cédrats confits et des pistaches. — Cela est bien dit, répondit Candide, mais il faut cultiver notre jardin."

little property produced much. True, Cunégonde was very ugly, but she became an excellent pastry cook; Paquette embroidered; the old woman took care of the linen. Not even Friar Giroflée failed to perform some service; he was a very good carpenter, and even became respectable; and Pangloss sometimes said to Candide: "All events are linked in the best of possible worlds; for, after all, if you had not been expelled from a handsome country house with great kicks in the behind for love of Mademoiselle Cunégonde, if you had not been brought before the Inquisition, if you had not traversed America on foot, if you had not given the Baron a good sword thrust, if you had not lost all your sheep from the good land of El Dorado, you would not be here eating candied citrons and pistachios." — "That is well said," replied Candide, "but we must cultivate our garden."